Recent Researches in the Music
of the Nineteenth and
Early Twentieth Centuries
Volume 15

Charles-Marie Widor

THE SYMPHONIES FOR ORGAN

Symphonie V

Edited by John R. Near

A-R Editions, Inc.

THE SYMPHONIES
FOR ORGAN

RECENT RESEARCHES IN THE MUSIC OF THE NINETEENTH AND EARLY TWENTIETH CENTURIES

Rufus Hallmark, general editor

A-R Editions, Inc., publishes seven series of musicological editions
that present music brought to light in the course of current research:

Recent Researches in the Music of the Middle Ages and Early Renaissance
Charles Atkinson, general editor

Recent Researches in the Music of the Renaissance
James Haar, general editor

Recent Researches in the Music of the Baroque Era
Christoph Wolff, general editor

Recent Researches in the Music of the Classical Era
Eugene K. Wolf, general editor

Recent Researches in the Music of the Nineteenth and Early Twentieth Centuries
Rufus Hallmark, general editor

Recent Researches in American Music
H. Wiley Hitchcock, general editor

Recent Researches in the Oral Traditions of Music
Philip V. Bohlman, general editor

Each *Recent Researches* edition is devoted to works
by a single composer or to a single genre of composition.
The contents are chosen for their potential interest to scholars
and performers, then prepared for publication according to the
standards that govern the making of all reliable historical editions.

Subscribers to any of these series, as well as patrons of subscribing institutions,
are invited to apply for information about the "Copyright-Sharing Policy"
of A-R Editions, Inc., under which policy any part of an edition
may be reproduced free of charge for study or performance.

For information contact

A-R EDITIONS, INC.
801 Deming Way
Madison, Wisconsin 53717

(608) 836-9000

RECENT RESEARCHES IN THE MUSIC OF THE NINETEENTH
AND EARLY TWENTIETH CENTURIES • VOLUME 15

Charles-Marie Widor

THE SYMPHONIES FOR ORGAN

Symphonie V

Edited by John R. Near

A-R Editions, Inc.
Madison

Charles-Marie Widor
THE SYMPHONIES FOR ORGAN

Edited by John R. Near

*Recent Researches in the Music
of the Nineteenth and Early Twentieth Centuries*

Opus 13	Symphonie I	in C Minor	Volume 11
	Symphonie II	in D Major	Volume 12
	Symphonie III	in E Minor	Volume 13
	Symphonie IV	in F Minor	Volume 14
Opus 42	Symphonie V	in F Minor	Volume 15
	Symphonie VI	in G Minor	Volume 16
	Symphonie VII	in A Minor	Volume 17
	Symphonie VIII	in B Major	Volume 18
Opus 70	*Symphonie gothique*		Volume 19
Opus 73	*Symphonie romane*		Volume 20

© 1993 by A-R Editions, Inc.
All rights reserved
Printed in the United States of America

Library of Congress Cataloging-in-Publication Data

Widor, Charles Marie, 1844–1937.
   [Symphonies, organ, no. 5, op. 42, no. 1, F minor]
   Symphonie V / Charles-Marie Widor ; edited by John R. Near.
   p. of music. — (The symphonies for organ / Charles-Marie Widor)
(Recent researches in the music of the nineteenth and early
twentieth centuries, ISSN 0193-5364 ; v. 15)
   Includes critical commentary and bibliographical references.
   ISBN 0-89579-276-1
   1. Symphonies (Organ) I. Near, John Richard, 1947– .
II. Series. III. Series: Widor, Charles Marie, 1844–1937.
Symphonies, organ (A-R Editions)
M2.R23834 vol. 15
[M8]   92-773130
                                  CIP
                                   M

Contents

Introduction
   The Sources   vii
   Editorial Policies   viii
   Widor's Registrations   ix
   Critical Commentary   ix

Widor's *Avant-propos*   xviii

Plates 1–2   xx

Symphonie V in F Minor
   I   2
   II   21
   III   35
   IV   46
   V. Toccata   48

Widor ca. 1891. One of two known poses taken by Touranchet, Paris, during one sitting. Henry Eymieu was a pupil of Widor, a composer, and a journalist (for *Le Ménestrel,* among others) who included Widor in his biographical series begun that year in *La Libre critique.* This photo is reproduced in *Revue pratique de liturgie et de musique sacrée* 6, nos. 61–62 (July–Aug. 1922), 46.

Introduction

From the time of their first publication, the organ symphonies of Charles-Marie Widor (1844–1937) have been recognized as masterpieces. Their influence on subsequent organ literature was once immense. As new generations of organ music became popular, however, there inevitably came a time when Widor's symphonies were neglected, often being judged outmoded. Even the French Romantic organ, perfected by Cavaillé-Coll and adored by musicians, was abused by later generations. Sufficient time was required to pass before Widor's art and instrument could be considered from a fresh and independent musical perspective. That perspective has evidently been achieved, for in recent years increasing numbers of musicians have begun evaluating the symphonies on their own terms, with the result that the works have enjoyed a notable resurgence of popularity. At the same time, the French Romantic organ has regained its former status.

Widor was perhaps his own most demanding critic. Following the first publication of each organ symphony, a continual transformation was effected by the composer through several revisions. In certain cases nearly six decades intervened between first and last versions of a work. Even after the final published edition, Widor continued to scrutinize his organ works, applying finishing touches to the pieces that have constituted his most enduring legacy.

This comprehensive edition of Widor's ten organ symphonies is the first to incorporate the many final emendations made by the composer in his own copies. Here also are presented for the first time together substantially or completely different earlier versions of passages, sections, and complete movements as they were conceived by Widor in the course of his long career. Using information in the Critical Commentary and the music of the Appendixes, musicians can perform or study these several earlier versions of each work.

The Preface to this edition (vol. 11, Symphonie I) provides a full discussion of the symphonies' genesis and historical environment as well as an extended discussion of editorial policy, sources, and performance. In this Introduction are provided information on performance sufficient to give the reader a sense of Widor's own preferences in registration and expression (including a translation of his foreword, or *avant-propos*), a conspectus of the sources, a summary of editorial policy, and a Critical Commentary.

The Sources

The original French editions and copies of these with corrections and emendations in Widor's hand form the basis for this critical edition. The locations of Widor's original holographs, if extant, are unknown. After extensively researching these works, the editor believes that all editions have surfaced, with one possible exception, noted in the Preface. These are listed here together with the identifying abbreviations used in the Critical Commentary and Appendixes. (More complete information on the sources appears in the Preface to the present edition.)

A	The first edition of opus 13, Symphonies I–IV, published in Paris in 1872 by the firm of J. Maho.
A'	A subsequent issue of *A* with minuscule alterations, published in 1879 by the firm of J. Hamelle together with the first editions of Symphonies V and VI.
B	The first complete issue of opus 42, comprising Symphonies V–VIII, together with the first major revision of opus 13, published in Paris in 1887 by Hamelle.
B'	A subsequent issue of *B* with small revisions to Symphonies I, VI, VII, and VIII, released between 1888 and 1892.
C	A new edition of opuses 13 and 42 (excepting Symphonie VI), published in 1901 and bearing the heading "New edition, revised, and entirely modified by the composer (1900–1901)."
C'	A subsequent issue of *C* that includes a new version of Symphonie VI and revisions to Symphonies I–V and VII–VIII, released by 1911.
D	A new edition of opuses 13 and 42, published in 1920, bearing the heading "New edition, revised, and entirely modified by the composer (1914–1918), (1920)."
E	The final published edition, again with revisions, issued 1928–29.
Emend 1	A copy of *B'* apparently used by Widor while preparing the revisions of edition *C* but also containing other emendations.
Emend 2	A bound and complete collection of single symphonies (representing variously the versions of editions *D* or *E*) with emendations made by Widor mostly after 1929, the year of edition *E*.
Emend 3	A copy of Symphonie V in the version of edition *D*, with numerous emendations by the composer, dated October 1927 in Widor's hand. This copy includes the revisions present

*Riem*5   in the 1929 edition, but it also contains further emendations, including some duplicated in *Emend* 2 and arguably entered after 1929.

*Riem*5   Berea, Ohio, The Riemenschneider Bach Institute at Baldwin-Wallace College, R 4008, is a single copy of Symphonie V in edition C owned by Albert Riemenschneider, Widor's most important American student. Riemenschneider studied with Widor in 1904–5, 1914, 1924, 1927, and 1930. In a letter to Riemenschneider dated 21 August 1927, Widor writes, "Five[?] times you've made the voyage across the Atlantic . . . to ask me about details on the feeling, the color, and the movement of my symphonies, which has proven the insufficiency of my indications. So, you're my collaborator."* While the score does clarify a few details, it is not clear which markings may be in Widor's hand.

Identical versions of movements in different editions are denoted in the Critical Commentary and the Appendixes by a slash between the identifying letters; for example, A/A'/B/B' means that a movement so identified remains the same through editions A, A', B, and B'.

Editorial Policies

Edition E (or, what amounts to the same thing, a version remaining constant through edition E) is generally taken as the principal source for the main body of this edition. Sources for Appendix variants are identified individually in the Critical Commentary. All departures from the source either are distinguished typographically (when they are editorial and straightforward) or are identified in the Critical Commentary (when they derive from other sources or are not explained by policies described here). There are two exceptions to the policy of bracketing: editorial ties, slurs, hairpins, and directs are dashed; editorial cautionary accidentals appear in reduced size; all other editorial additions are enclosed in brackets.

The original French prints are themselves replete with cautionary accidentals, usually provided to cancel flats and sharps in previous measures. All except repetitious cautionary accidentals within a measure are preserved in this edition.

In the Critical Commentary the three staves of a system are indexed 1, 2, and 3, in order from top to bottom. Occasionally staff 1 in the source editions is congested, while an empty or nearly empty staff lies directly below. In such contexts this edition sometimes tacitly transfers left-hand voices to the open staff 2.

In the sources, indications of dynamics under staff 1 are sometimes duplicated under staves 2 or 3 or both in contexts where the Pédale and other manuals would have to share those dynamics in any event. The editor has suppressed most of these redundant dynamic indications. In addition, the old engravings frequently place dynamic indications over staff 1 because of space limitations on the page; conversely, they sometimes place tempo indications between staves 1 and 2 for the same reason. This edition tacitly regularizes the position of all such marks, putting dynamic indications within the system and tempo indications above it. There is an obvious exception to this rule: namely, when a dynamic is meant to apply to one staff alone, it appears closest to the affected voice(s)—therefore, sometimes above staff 1. Because Widor indicated registration and dynamics somewhat differently in editions A and A', the source placement of the relevant signs is preserved in appendix extracts from them.

Widor indicated staccato with the dot up to the late 1890s, but he favored the wedge thereafter. The two signs become mixed in passages partially revised by the composer after about 1900 (the period of edition C). Widor's pedagogical works on organ music reveal that both signs had the same significance for him. In the present edition all wedges are tacitly changed to dots in pieces conceived before Widor's change of orthography; wedges are retained in movements composed after the change.

Beaming in the original French editions is sometimes used to clarify phrasing. Beaming in the new edition follows that of the sources except when, under certain stringent conditions spelled out in detail in the Preface to this edition (see vol. 11, Symphonie I), it can be shown with great probability that inconsistencies arise through oversight or through adherence to an outmoded convention for beaming.

Characteristic of Widor's musical orthography is its attention to inner contrapuntal voices in every musical texture. At times this leads to a phalanx of stems all aiming for the same metrical position. Stemming in the new edition generally follows that of the sources, since the appearance of counterpoint, even in predominantly homophonic textures, conveys much of the "feel" and attitude proper to Widor's symphonies. Departures from the source are made only in clearly defined circumstances spelled out in detail in the Preface to this edition. In general, the number of voices in a measure is kept constant. In clearly homophonic contexts, where Widor himself is less strict, inconsistencies in the number of voices in a measure are usually allowed to stand. All editorial rests are bracketed. Stems added by analogy with parallel or closely similar passages are not bracketed, but the source reading is reported in a critical note. All other stems added to clarify inconsistent voicing are bracketed. Infrequently, superfluous rests or stems in the sources are tacitly removed to keep part writing consistent in a measure.

In conformity with accepted practice of that era, the original French editions of Widor's organ symphonies provide double barlines for all changes of key and for

---

*Berea, Ohio, The Riemenschneider Bach Institute at Baldwin-Wallace College, Letters from Widor to Riemenschneider.

some changes of meter. In this edition these are converted to single barlines unless there is also a new tempo, a new texture, or some other sign of a structural subdivision.

Reference to pitch in the Critical Commentary is made as follows: middle C = c'; C above middle C = c''; C below middle C = c; two octaves below middle C = C. Successive pitches are separated by commas, simultaneous pitches by virgules.

Widor's Registrations

Widor generally indicated registrations by family of tone-color instead of exact stop nomenclature. In so doing he never intended to condone willful or indiscriminate interpretations of his registrational plans. He had a particular horror of kaleidoscopic stop changes and artlessly haphazard use of the Expression pedal. To those who indulged in a continual manipulation of the stops or Expression pedal, he habitually advised, "I beg you, no magic lantern effects." Barring the unfortunate necessity of making certain adaptations to varying organs, one should no more alter the "orchestration" of a Widor organ symphony than change or dress up the instrumentation of a Beethoven symphony. Clearly, the faithful realization of Widor's registrational plan is essential to the presentation of these works as the composer heard them. Beyond this, knowledge of the Cavaillé-Coll organ, the instrument preferred by Widor, will also prove useful to the performer intent on maximum fidelity to the composer's intention. A discussion of this organ and its constraints on performance can be found in the Preface to this edition (see vol. 11, Symphonie I).

To indicate the registration he wanted, Widor adopted a relatively simple shorthand system: **G** represents Grand-orgue (Great); **P** Positif (Positive); **R** Récit (Swell); **Péd.** Pédale (Pedal). Fonds are the foundation stops; Anches the chorus reed stops as well as all correlative stops included in the Jeux de combinaison. Pitch designations are self-evident.

When found above, within, or directly below the keyboard staves, a single letter instructs the organist to play on that particular uncoupled manual. When two or three letters are combined in these locations, the first designates the manual to play on, the second and subsequent letters what is to be coupled to it. For example, **GPR** instructs the organist to play on the Grand-orgue with the Positif and Récit coupled to it; **PR** tells one to play on the Positif with the Récit coupled to it; and so on.

When found under the lowest staff, one or more letters designate which manuals are to be coupled to the Pédale. When Widor employs only a dynamic marking in the course of the Pédale line, the performer should determine at his own discretion which Pédale coupler needs to be retired or reintroduced.

All crescendo and decrescendo indications, no matter how lengthy, are to be effected only by manipulation of the Expression pedal, unless the crescendo leads to a *fff*. In that case the Jeux de combinaison of each division are to be brought into play successively on strong beats: first those of the Récit (perhaps already on), then those of the Positif (sometimes indicated with a *ff*), and finally those of the Grand-orgue and Pédale on the *fff*. For the decrescendo they are to be retired in reverse order on weak beats.

Critical Commentary

The symphonies V and *gothique* seem to have been Widor's personal favorites; he often performed them complete, and he recorded movements from them at Saint-Sulpice in April 1932.[*] Writing for *Le Ménestrel* in 1880, Eugène Gigout suggested that organists could look to Widor's "remarkable" new symphonies (the fifth and sixth) as examples of "works of real value."[†] Symphonie V, written when the thirty-four-year-old composer was in the middle of his most fecund compositional period, has been a staple of the organ's literature ever since. Had Widor composed no other organ music, this symphony alone would have assured him a permanent place in the repertoire. A full account of the composition and publication history of this work can be found under First Performances and Publications in the Preface to Symphonie I of this edition.

I

The first movement is cast as a free theme and variations; the term *fantasy-variations* has been aptly applied to it.[‡] The opening measures of the theme bear a striking resemblance to those of the twelfth etude in Robert Schumann's *Symphonische Etuden*, opus 13, for piano. Widor's own expansive theme (mm. 1–41) unfolds in four repeated four-measure phrases plus a concluding, repeated eight-measure phrase. Between three imaginative variations (mm. 42–73, 74–113, 114–50) and the fantasylike development (mm. 181–251), an episode of solemn four-part writing (mm. 151–80) is interposed. The development leads to a climactic treatment (mm. 252–91) of the thematic material. Expanding the structure of the old form, Widor succeeded in bringing it a new image.

There are four similar versions: A¹, B/B¹, C/C¹/D, and E. Edition E is the principal source. Two sources of autograph revisions exist for this symphony: *Emend* 2 and *Emend* 3 (for a discussion of these sources, see the Preface to this edition: vol. 11, Symphonie I, Sources, "Autograph Revisions," xvi–xvii). The present edition follows *Emend* 3 primarily; *Emend* 2 is referred to when it provides corrections or clarifications that, for one reason

---

[*] Gramophone (His Master's Voice) DB-4856; also: *Orgues et organistes français en 1930*, EMI 2 C 153-16411/5.
[†] Eugène Gigout, "Quelques publications nouvelles d'orgue et de plain-chant," *Le Ménestrel* 46 (1880): 44.
[‡] Albert Riemenschneider, "Program Notes on the Widor 'Symphonies,'" *American Organist* 8 (1925): 266.

or another, did not get transmitted to *Emend* 3 (see pl. 1, which reproduces the cover of this autograph source).

Revisions in editions after *A'* brought about some minor changes in articulation (mm. 3, 7, 27, 28, and 31); a brief transfer of the pedal part to the manuals (m. 32, beat 4, through m. 35, beat 1), with concomitant adjustments in the manual part writing; small alterations in the pedal line (m. 125, beat 4, through m. 136, beat 1, and mm. 186–91); and some cosmetic rewriting (mm. 73, 121, and 189). More interesting are the revisions of tempo, registration, and other interpretive details. For instance, whereas edition *A'* has no metronome marks, all eight symphonies in edition *B* have these supplied by Widor. By the time of edition *C*, the composer had turned against excessively fast tempos. This attitude is evidenced in the present movement by a slower opening metronome mark and the removal of all but one of eight interior metronome marks (most of which steadily increase the tempo after m. 180) added in edition *B*. This movement offers an excellent opportunity to watch Widor's thinking evolve on such particulars. Accordingly, the most noteworthy of them are listed here.

Tempos, Registrations, and Interpretive Marks in Editions *A'* through *D*

The opening mark is half note equals 76 in *B/B'*. M. 32, staff 3, beat 4 has **PG** in *A'* and *B/B'* (as mentioned above, the lowest manual voice is played on the Pédale here). This directive is a bit enigmatic since normally **G** would precede **P**; perhaps it is an engraver's error for **Péd. G** (to lighten this sonority, notice that Widor returns to staccato markings for staff 3 when staves 1 and 2 return to **R** at m. 36, beat 4). Without pursuing further the possible ramifications of this coupler directive—which are not at issue in the present edition—one may, nonetheless, recognize it as a telltale sign suggesting that the lack of any coupler directive at the beginning of the movement is intentional.

M. 41, staves 1 and 2, beat 4, the registration directive is "Flûte 4, Bourdon 16" (staff 3 has no "Flûte 8' solo") in *A'* through *D*. M. 49, beat 4 has no *mf* in *A'* and *B/B'*. M. 50, beat 4 has no *p* in *A'* and *B/B'*. Mm. 52–53 have no crescendo hairpin or following *mf* in *A'* and *B/B'*. M. 54, beat 4 has no *p* in *A'* and *B/B'*. Mm. 56–57 have no crescendo hairpin in *A'* and *B/B'*. M. 57, staff 3, the registration directive is "Basses 4, 16" (no **Péd. R**) in *A'* through *D*. M. 73 has no Adagio and Tempo I indications, the different staff-2 part is marked **P** and *riten.* (before the measure was revised, playing the part on **P** allowed the preparation of the Récit anches on beat 3), and staff 3 has no "Fonds 16', 8', 4'" in *A'* through *D*; staff 1, beat 4 has *p* in *A'* and *B/B'*. M. 97 has no fermatas in *A'* and *B/B'*.

M. 105, beat 4, staff 3 has no registration directive in *A'* and *B/B'*. M. 113, beat 4 has half note equals 66 in *B/B'*; the registration directives are "**R** Flûte 4, Bourdon 16" in *A'* through *E*, "**P** Montre et Unda maris 8" in *A'* and *B/B'* (**P** is "Gambe et Unda maris 8" in *C* through *E*—Widor likely changed the former peculiar combination to reflect a more common stop disposition), "**Péd.** Basses 4, 16" in *A'* and *B/B'*. M. 146 has no *cresc.* in *A'* and *B/B'*. M. 148 has no *cresc.* in *A'*. M. 151, beat 2 has quarter note equals 104 in *B/B'*; staves 1 and 2, manual directive and dynamic mark are **G** { *f* (**G** remains Fonds 16', 8', 4' from the beginning) in *A'*; manual directive and dynamic mark are **GPR** { *ff* with registration directive "**GPR** Fonds 4, 8, 16" in *B* through *E*; staff 3, dynamic mark is *f* in *A'* and *ff* in *B* through *E*. M. 164, staves 1 and 2 have no **PR** directive in *A'*. Mm. 167–68 have no decrescendo hairpin in *A'* and *B/B'*. M. 168 has caesuras for all three staves before beat 4 and no **G** { *f* in *A'* (*B/B'* has **G** without dynamic mark). M. 176, staves 1 and 2 have no **PR** directive in *A'* and *B/B'*. M. 178 has no *rit.* in *A'*. Mm. 178, beat 4, through m. 179 have no decrescendo hairpin in *A'* and *B/B'*. M. 180, beat 4 has no registration directive in *A'*. M. 181, beat 1 has quarter note equals 96 in *B* through *E*—this clearly would begin with the upbeat to the measure. M. 191, staff 2 has no registration directive in *A'* through *E*. M. 192, beat 1 has quarter note equals 100 in *B/B'*—to begin with the upbeat to the measure. Mm. 194 and 198 have no *agitato* in *A'*.

M. 202, beat 1 has quarter note equals 112 in *B/B'*. M. 218, beat 2 has *poco riten.* in *B/B'*. M. 220, beat 1 has quarter note equals 132 in *B/B'*—to begin with the upbeat to the measure—where *C/C'/D* has *con brio*. M. 227, beat 2 has *animato* in *B/B'*. M. 228, beat 1 has quarter note equals 144 in *B/B'*. M. 257 has no *poco allarg.* in *A'*. M. 259 has no *con brio* in *A'*. M. 275, beat 4 has quarter note equals 152 in *B/B'*; staves 1–3 have no *mf* in *A'* and *B/B'*. Mm. 278–79 have no crescendo in *A'* and *B/B'*. Mm. 282–83 have no *rit.* and *a tempo* in *A'*. M. 284 has *agitato* in *B/B'*. M. 289 has no *fff* in *A'* and *B/B'*. M. 290, beat 4 has tenuto dashes instead of fermatas in *A'* and *B/B'*—see report for m. 290 in the Critical Notes.

Performance Insights

Although it is not the policy of this edition to discuss Widor's pedagogic ideology, here and in the last two movements citations from his preface to the Bach organ works offer insights that seem apropos to the material at hand. Widor's comments on his phrasing of certain note groupings appear applicable to the two-note slurrings found throughout the third variation (m. 113, beat 4, through m. 149). Such suggestive marks, Widor writes, only serve to "mentally" group the notes.

> We say *mentally* because it is quite necessary to keep from detaching the sounds from each other. The skillfulness [of the player] lies in making the intentions of the composer felt either by accentuations of duration or by subtleties of touch.*

---

*Charles-Marie Widor, preface to *Jean-Sébastien Bach: Oeuvres complètes pour orgue*, 2 (New York: G. Schirmer, 1914), vii.

And in another instance he states:

> Let's repeat here what we have repeated many times, namely that these slurs represent the bowings of the orchestra, and that on the organ the player is not at all to take account of them. We indicate them only for a more immediate understanding of the idea.*

CRITICAL NOTES

Upbeat to m. 1, staff 3, note has no staccato in secondary-set prints of E (see Sources in the Preface to this edition, vol. 11, Symphonie I, xiv–xv)—several staccato dots in this movement faded from later prints of edition E as the plates deteriorated. M. 12, staves 1 and 2, beats 1–3, quarter-note dyads are stemmed together —this is inconsistent with the four-part writing of the phrase (m. 8, beat 4, through m. 12, beat 3) and with similar m. 263, where four-part writing continues with separate stemming. M. 16, staves 1 and 2, beats 1–3, see report for similar m. 12. M. 19, staff 1, upper voice, slur begins on (staccato) beat 4 of m. 18—edition follows analogous m. 270 and similar phrasings throughout (see, e.g., m. 8, beat 4, through m. 10, beat 3; and m. 16, beat 4, through m. 18, beat 3). M. 23, staff 1, upper voice, slur begins on (staccato) beat 4 of m. 22—see report for analogous m. 19. M. 24, staff 1, upper voice, note 1 has staccato in all editions—an error. M. 31, staff 1, beat 3, f' has no dot in any edition—although the note is stemmed with a dotted quarter note, the lack of the dot may be correct. M. 34, staff 1, lower voice, note 1 is dotted in editions C through E—an error; when the part writing of A' and B/B' was revised for C, the dot was not deleted. M. 36, staff 3, note 3, editorial staccato follows A' and B/B'—the dot likely faded from later editions. M. 40, staff 2, beat 4, the dyad is stemmed together—edition follows parallel m. 32, beat 4. M. 49, staff 1, lower voice, beat 3 has eighth rest—an error, as this momentarily accounts for four voices. M. 50, staff 2, note 1 has incoming slur from m. 49 (in previous system with no outgoing slur) in all editions—an error. M. 97, staff 1, beat 4, e' has no natural in any edition—edition follows *Emend* 2 (this natural is not marked in *Emend* 3).

M. 105, the single **G** manual directive is questionable. In many instances throughout Widor's organ works, after the initial appearance of a manual directive (such as **GPR**) he uses its abbreviation (**G**) as an expedient, even when, sometimes, it causes ambiguity.† Here in previous measures Widor consistently indicates **GR** for passages to be played on the Grand-orgue manual. To abbreviate the directive at this point seems peculiar; whether it is an engraver's error that Widor never corrected or an intentional uncoupling of **R** from **G** must be decided by the performer.

M. 113, beat 3, edition E has a barline after this beat—an error; the measure is split so that beat 4 is at the top of the next page in all editions—the engraver evidently did not take this into account when supplying what appeared to be a (necessary or) missing barline; beat 4, the registration directives are "**R** Flûte 4, Bourdon 16, **P** Gambe et Unda maris 8"—whereas both *Emend* 2 and *Emend* 3 revise the Récit registration, only *Emend* 3 revises the Positif registration; both emendations are marked in ink on page 8 of *Emend* 3 (a page indicated on the cover for correction). The only other mark on the page is for staff 3, where Widor wrote and circled *8* in blue pencil—this mark is a second cautionary reminder for the Flûte 8' directives given at m. 105, beat 4, and, in the source, m. 113, beat 1. One might hope to find in Widor's use of writing utensils some pattern betraying layers of revision. This is not possible in the present movement; most pages marked for revision contain a combination of ink and blue (sometimes red) pencil markings. Whereas the emendations from every other page indicated on the cover of *Emend* 3 were transmitted to edition E, curiously, none were from page 8; possibly they were entered after the publication of E. These simpler and less colorful registrations are in keeping with Widor's later preferences and are appropriate to the style of his later works. The editor feels that the original registrations are more felicitous in the present movement.

M. 118, staff 1, beat 4, the editorial flat is confirmed by *Riem*5. M. 120, staff 2, beats 2 and 4, and staff 3, note 2, compare parallel m. 143—the subtle differences here raise the issue of authorial intention or engraver's error; although the two passages remained curiously at variance through all editions and emendations, the reading in m. 143, staff 2, seems correct since the slurred two-note figures are consistently minor seconds throughout the phrase; *Riem*5 also confirms c'-sharp in m. 120; unfortunately, for staff 3, note 2, *Riem*5 has no alterations, and without Widor's holographs it is not possible to know if the difference is attributable to an engraver's error—the editor doubts that Widor intentionally created two readings.

M. 122, staff 1, beat 4, the editorial flat is added by analogy with sequential m. 124—the editor believes the omission of the flat to be an oversight. M. 136, staff 2, beat 1 is staccato quarter note (followed by half rest) in all editions—the editorial alteration of the note value and removal of the staccato dot conform to Widor's policy of simultaneous attack and release of manual and pedal notes (this alteration is also seen in *Riem*5); when Widor revised the staff-3 part for edition C he probably overlooked the resulting discrepancy between staves 2 and 3, beat 1, and although a staccato note usually loses half its value according to Widor's practice, the notational discrepancy could lead to misinterpretation (see m. 133, beat 3, where the note values accord). M. 141, staff 1, see report for m. 118.

M. 146, staff 2, beat 2 (and m. 148, staves 1 and 2, beat 2), since the Positif is often unexpressive, the *cresc.* indications are ambiguous—they may address a problem that arises only with the registrations given before *Emend* 3; in the earlier versions "cresc." could be

---

*Ibid., xvii.
†Ibid.

interpreted as suggesting the addition of another 8' stop to reinforce the line as it descends into the bass range (recall that Widor first specified "Montre et Unda maris 8'" and later "Gambe et Unda maris 8'")—since the Unda maris begins at c, in these registration schemes, the line will weaken as it moves below the Unda maris range, unless reinforced.* When Widor revised the registration in *Emend* 3, he may have neglected to delete these crescendo directives; but since this is not certain, the performer will have to decide how best to deal with them. M. 148, beat 2, through m. 150, staves 1 and 2, the division of the four-note groups between the staves is best construed as alternating hands rather than alternating manuals—Widor's beaming together of the beat groups confirms this.

M. 151, staves 1 and 2, beat 2, the registration directive and dynamic mark for **GPR** are "Fonds 4, 8, 16" *ff* in editions *B* through *E*—whereas both *Emend* 2 and *Emend* 3 revise the registration directive, only *Emend* 3 revises the dynamic mark; staff 3, beat 2, the coupler directive is **Péd. G** in all editions (it was never revised), the dynamic mark is *ff* in editions *B* through *E*—in *Emend* 3 Widor returns to the *f* of edition *A'*. M. 168, the manual directive is **G** in editions *B* through *E*—in this instance the directive is likely being used as an abbreviation for **GPR**, as given in m. 151; see report for m. 105. M. 191, staff 2 has no registration directive—edition follows *Emend* 3. M. 193, staff 1, beat 1, editorial staccato follows editions *A'* through *D*—the dot faded in *E*.

Mm. 204–9, staff 2, although Widor did not continue to mark the staccato articulation, the editor feels that its continuation is appropriate here and in mm. 213–19, beat 2. M. 227, staves 1 and 2 have *diminuendo* in *Emend* 2, beginning on the anacrusis to beat 2. M. 231, staves 1 and 2 have *p* on the anacrusis to beat 4, and staff 3 has *p* on beat 4—these dynamic marks are then crossed out along with an indefinite staff-3 directive ("**Péd.** Fonds"?) in *Emend* 2. M. 235, staves 1 and 2 have *p* on the anacrusis to beat 4 (*dimin.* is crossed out) and staff 3 has *p* on beat 4 in *Emend* 2—the editor suggests that these dynamic marks could be utilized in lieu of the second *dimin.*, found in m. 239. M. 251, staves 1 and 2, beat 4, manual directive is **G** in all editions—in this instance there can be no question that the directive is being used as an abbreviation for **GPR** (see reports for mm. 105 and 168); although the directive is placed on beat 4, the staff-2 anacrusis note (b-natural) would be played on **GPR**; because Widor did not break the beam in staff 1, beat 3, between notes 3 and 4, no articulation is suggested and it may be smoother to move the right hand to the Grand orgue on beat 4, as indicated by the directive.

M. 262, staff 1, beats 2 and 3, lower voice is two g" eighth notes, a"[-natural] quarter note in *Emend* 1. M. 263, staff 1, upper voice, note 1, editorial staccato follows analogous m. 12, where the dyad of beat 1 is stemmed together in the source and has a staccato dot—see report for m. 12. M. 266, staff 1, beats 2 and 3 are marked with a dagger in *Emend* 1, suggesting a similar alteration to that given for m. 262; staff 2, beats 1 through 3, the dyads are stemmed together—separate stemming follows similar m. 262 and the majority practice of the passage. M. 267, staff 1, beats 1–3, the dyads are stemmed together—this is inconsistent with the four-part writing of the phrase and with similar m. 263, where four-part writing continues with separate stemming; beat 1, editorial staccatos follow analogous m. 12—see report for m. 12. M. 290, staff 2, beat 4 has tenuto dash below chord—an error; the tenuto dashes in staves 1 and 3 were deleted when the fermatas were introduced in edition *C*.

II

The buoyant Hautbois and Flûte melodies lend a folk-like lyricism to the second movement. There are three versions: *A'*, *B*/*B'*/*C*/*C'*/*D*, and *E*. In addition, Widor later published a version for piano that is dramatically different (and quite pianistic).† In editions *A'* through *D* the form of the movement is a perfectly balanced A B A. Widor apparently felt that the full repetition of the A section was too long. Accordingly, *Emend* 3 and edition *E* cut seventy-six measures from the second A section; the cut corresponds to measures 30 through 105 of the first A section. (*Emend* 2 shows a less substantial cut in the second A section: it corresponds to mm. 59–74 of the first A section; Widor mistakenly marked the end of the cut one bar too early—it should be after m. 75.) Furthermore, in the B section Widor removed repeat bars enclosing measures 128 through 199 (the deletion is marked in both *Emend* 2 and *Emend* 3). Edition *E* is the principal source. Variants are from *Emend* 3 and, in one instance, from *Emend* 2, where its corroborative reading is clearer.

In *Emend* 3 Widor marked the cut in the second A section by crossing out measures 275 through 350 and making revisions to measure 274 so that it would connect properly to measure 351 (because of the second ending at the repeat in editions *A'* through *D*, the measure numbers are two higher than in edition *E* and the present edition after m. 199). He made no other revisions in the measures before or after the cut. J. Hamelle reengraved the shortened A section (from m. 242 in the present edition) to fit onto two pages. In so doing the engraver made numerous errors and omissions in measures that were not being revised but were only being reengraved to fit the new space constraints; these are reported in the Critical Notes. Had Widor lived to see another published edition of this symphony, many of these errors would undoubtedly have been corrected. It

---

*The Unda maris 8' is incorrectly identified as beginning at d in table 2 of the Preface to this edition, vol. 11, Symphonie I, xxii.

†*Conte d'Automne pour piano*, without opus number, published in Paris in 1904 by J. Hamelle (plate no. J.5023 H).

is especially unfortunate that no copy of Symphonie V in edition E has come to us from Widor's personal scores.

As often happens in these symphonies, staccato dots are at variance from print to print and in parallel sections of a movement. This is almost always the result of deteriorating plates and engraving errors rather than authorial intent or revision, though certainly some staccatos are lacking as a result of the composer's oversight. The editor also believes that Widor assumed the player would maintain the articulation of a given figuration or pattern after it was marked in an initial occurrence.* In the present movement most editorial staccato dots have been supplied after consulting either one of the parallel A sections in editions A' through D (especially the earlier of these, where fading was not yet a problem) or the immediate context or both. (Examples of immediate context are m. 42, staff 3, upper voice, note 7, and mm. 95–96, staff 2, upper voice.) In the case of the pedal, however, notes of quarter-note value or less should probably be played staccato throughout this movement unless slurred or marked with a tenuto. (Exceptions may occur in mm. 107–20, 144–58, and 274–87.)

To play version B/B'/C/C'/D, reinstate the repeat of mm. 128–97 and the first and second endings (mm. 198–201) given in the critical notes, then substitute mm. 7–126 for mm. 250–93 with the following changes for the second A section: m. 29, staff 3, note 1 is B-flat staccato eighth note (this discrepancy was undoubtedly an oversight); m. 126, staff 1 has no f', staff 2 has f half note (stemmed up and down), staff 3 has F half note.

Edition A' differs from version B/B'/C/C'/D as follows (the reading of the second A section is the same as that of the first A section reported here). M. 38, staff 1, note 2 has *p*, and there is no crescendo hairpin. M. 42, staff 1, beat 1 has decrescendo hairpin followed by **pp**, located over staff 2, note 1. M. 62, staff 1 has **pp**, located over staff 2, upper voice, note 1, instead of in m. 63. M. 67, staff 2 is quarter rest, eighth rest, d" staccato eighth note, and there is no slur extending to m. 71, note 1. Mm. 68–69, staff 2, notes are staccato (the staccato dots are omitted after edition B'). M. 82, staff 1, beat 2, note 2 has **pp**, and there is no crescendo hairpin. M. 83, staff 1 has no *f*. M. 94, staff 1 has no decrescendo hairpin. M. 95, staff 1 has no **pp**. M. 200 (second ending—see example 1), beat 2 has *poco più lento* directive. Mm. 220, 228, and 236 (the measure numbers are two greater in editions A' through D) have no *meno vivo* directives.

CRITICAL NOTES

M. 6, staff 1, editorial dynamic mark follows analogous m. 249 (return of the A section). Mm. 18–19, staff 3, slur extends to the end of m. 18 (= end of system) but does not continue to m. 19, note 1 (= beginning of next system)—there are other instances where the engraver apparently neglected to carry slurs or ties over to a new system or page (e.g. mm. 127–28, 158–59, and in the second A section in editions A' through D, mm. 263–64 and 361–62. M. 61, staff 1, *f* is on beat 1 instead of beat 2—an error; beat 2 has *riten.* in editions A' through D—it is crossed out in *Emend* 3 and omitted from E. M. 62, second half of beat 2 has *a tempo* in all editions—this should have been omitted from edition E (see report for m. 61); staff 2, the short slur between staccato d"-natural and staccato c"-sharp (in m. 63) is in *Emend* 3 and edition E—it serves to emphasize the harmonic shift to A major after two previous parallel passages in A-flat major (at mm. 42 and 50); the longer slur extending through m. 64 follows *Emend* 3 and the phrasing in parallel mm. 42–44.

M. 71, the change of manual to **G** is between beat 2, notes 2 and 3—edition follows change of manual in similar m. 54; the staccato articulation ending after beat 1 suggests the change on beat 2 as more appropriate. M. 80, staff 1, editorial staccatos follow parallel m. 325 (second A section in editions A' through D) as well as the pattern in the previous measure. M. 82, staff 1, notes 1 and 2 are staccato in all editions—edition follows parallel m. 327 (second A section in editions A' through D) as well as the pattern in the previous two beats. M. 87, staff 2, note 2 has no upstem—edition follows editions A' through D. M. 94, staff 3, slur ends on note 3 in all editions—edition follows parallel m. 339 (second A section in editions A' through D).

M. 127, staves 2 and 3, slurs extend to the end of m. 127 (= end of system) but do not continue to m. 128, note 1 (= beginning of next system)—see report for m. 18. M. 152, staff 1, the return to **G** is not marked in any edition (Widor apparently overlooked the ambiguity of manual designation that arises when the source returns from four to three staves with a new system beginning at m. 149)—*Riem*5 has **G** inserted.

Mm. 198–202 of editions A' through D are given in example 1 (see commentary above for edition A', m. 200). Because the second ending is omitted in edition E, m. 202 in the figure corresponds to m. 200 in E. When Widor deleted the repeat in the B section, he created an ambiguity regarding manuals and couplers. In *Emend* 3, m. 128 has "pas de reprise" (no repeat) with a deletion mark and a dagger over the repeat sign at the beginning of the measure; in m. 199 the repeat dots on the double bar are crossed out and there is a deletion mark. *Emend* 2 shows the revision more completely: in the first ending (mm. 198–99) the ending bracket above staff 1 and the repeat dots on the double bar are crossed out, and "pas de reprise" is written in the margin; m. 199, staff 1, beat 2 has an eighth rest written over the quarter rest and then a'[-flat] eighth note slurred over the barline; mm. 200–201 are crossed out except for the a'[-flat] eighth note *and* the coupler directive beneath staff 3. In mm. 200–223 (the measure numbers are those of edition E and the present edition) the single letter **G** is used in-

---

*For example, in mm. 12–13 the staff-3 notes are marked staccato, and those of mm. 16–17 are not—to the editor this seems to be a pointless and unintentional difference; also notice in similar mm. 16 and 92 that note 2 is staccato only in the latter measure.

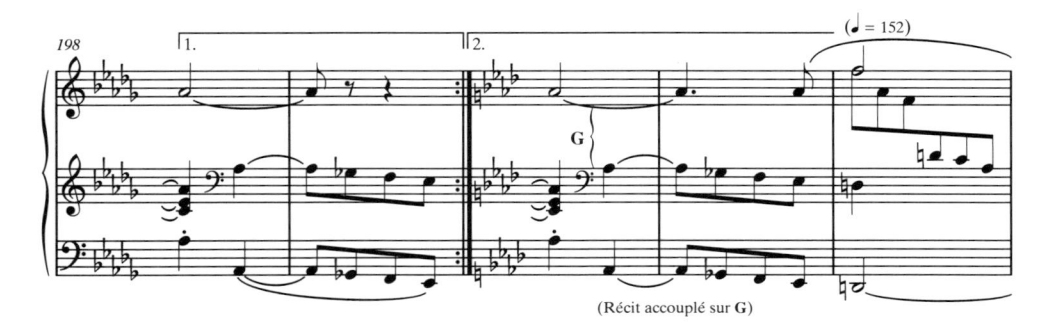

Example 1. II, mm. 198–202, in editions A' through D.

stead of **GR**; this is another example of Widor abbreviating a directive after it has been established—here, by the coupler directive beneath mm. 200–201, staff 3 (see discussion in the Critical Notes for movement I, mm. 105, 168, 251). That **G** and **R** are coupled in mm. 200–235 is confirmed by the "G solo" directive in m. 236, staff 2. In edition *E*, the lack of the coupler directive and/or manual indications in the transitional passage causes an ambiguity that can only be clarified by examining the earlier editions and *Emend* 2. Because Widor has given a one-beat rest in the middle of m. 199, staff 1, it seems best to couple the manuals there rather than at m. 198, beat 2, as might be suggested from the original reading; by keeping the left hand on **R** through m. 200, beat 1, a smooth transition is effected. M. 200, staff 2 (= beginning of new system) has treble clef—an error, resulting from the reengraving of the passage when the second ending was deleted in *E*.

M. 236, staff 2 has *meno vivo* in editions *B* through *E*—edition follows *Emend* 3. M. 260, staff 2, note 4 is a[-flat]—this is certainly an engraver's error made when the second A section was reengraved in its shorter version—edition follows analogous m. 17 and m. 262 in editions *A'* through *D*; staff 3, notes lack eighth-flags in edition *E*—further evidence of the engraver's errors. Mm. 261–62, staff 3, slur extends to the end of m. 261 (= end of system) but does not continue to m. 262, note 1 (= beginning of new system)—edition follows analogous m. 339 (second A section in editions *A'* through *D*). M. 266, staff 2, upper voice, beat 2 has a[-flat], c', e'[-flat]—this is certainly another engraver's error made when the second A section was reengraved; edition follows analogous m. 23 and m. 268 in editions *A'* through *D*. M. 267, staff 1, notes 1 and 2 are not beamed together—edition follows analogous m. 24 and m. 269 in editions *A'* through *D*. Mm. 272–73, the editorial emendations follow mm. 105–6 and are contextually correct for what follows—the cut material following the connective measure (corresponding to m. 29 in the first A section) is different. M. 276, staff 2, **P** is given by the dynamic mark *p* in edition *E*—an engraver's error; edition follows analogous m. 109.

III

With its central position in the symphony, this ternary-form movement functions as a sort of scherzo, but one of unique character; the A sections are broad and stately, the B section nervous and intense. Widor's working out of the thematic material is especially inventive: the opening theme of the A section transforms into both the melody and pedal ostinato of the B section. Such an ostinato is striking in organ music of this period; it presages what Louis Vierne was to do in the first movement of his Symphonie II over twenty years later. Widor made virtually no revisions in this music,* though *Emend* 3 brought the correction of one accidental to *E*. Edition *E* is the principal source.

Exceptionally, the registration directive includes instructions for couplers: "Tous les claviers accouplés sur **G**" (All manuals coupled to **G**). In the present edition, **GPR** is indicated throughout the movement instead of Widor's abbreviation **G**. Though not specified in the directive, the editor has also indicated **PR** throughout, instead of **P**, in the belief that the usual concept of terraced tonal levels (**GPR**, **PR**, **R**) is in operation and in view of the initial Pédale-coupler directive of **GPR**; also, in measures 172 and 174 the Positif sounds strangely barren without the Récit and its Anches 16', 8', 4' coupled to it.

Critical Notes

Mm. 35–36, staff 1, upper voice, note the difference between the phrasing here and in analogous mm. 201–2—the editor doubts that the discrepancy is intentional and suggests adopting the phrasing of mm. 201–2 for mm. 35–36. M. 103, staff 1, beat 1 has no e''' in secondary sets of edition *E*—over time it faded from the plates. M. 153, staff 1, upper voice, note 3 is f'' in all editions—edition follows analogous m. 107 and also m. 157. M. 190, staff 1, beat 3, editorial phrasing follows analogous m. 24. M. 196, staff 2, upper voice, note has no dot in any edition—an error. M. 198, staff 1, editorial extension of the slur to upper voice, note 1, follows analogous m. 32.

Mm. 205–6, staff 1, editorial extension of the slur follows analogous mm. 39–40—since m. 204 is at the end of a system, the engraver probably neglected to continue the slur (for other examples of this, see critical reports for II, m. 18). M. 219, staff 2, beat 3, notes are

---

*M. 71, edition *A'* has *Poco più mosso* instead of the directive at m. 69.

stemmed together—edition follows analogous m. 53. M. 223, staff 1, editorial extension of the slur to upper voice, note 1, follows analogous m. 57. M. 233, beat 2, the registration directive for **P** is given at m. 234, beat 2, in all editions—since this directive only effects the addition of Fonds 16' (Fonds 8' and 4' already being drawn), it seems more logical to locate it here.

IV

The thirty-one measures that make up the fourth movement create a moment of repose before the torrent to be unleashed in the following Toccata. The four-part manual texture is occasionally augmented by entries of a 4' Pédale Flûte solo, the first such entry making a canon at the octave with the soprano voice. Widor tired of music with pedal lines that always droned in an unendurable monotony of 16' tone.* Here he ingeniously expands the function of the Pédale; while retaining its 4' solo character, he simultaneously enriches the manual texture by use of double pedal and the successive entries of 8' and 16' pitches in the final measures. This is but one of many movements where Widor assigned an unusual role to the Pédale. The movement exists in four nearly identical versions: A', B/B', C, and C'/D/E. Edition E is the principal source.

Examination of the revisions made in this movement during a period of about twenty-five years—the time between editions A' and C'—reveals just a few small refinements or corrections. Edition C differs from version C'/D/E by one note: in measure 31, staff 3, edition C has a middle-voice c whole note—an error, the note not being deleted after the revision of edition B'. In B/B', measure 30, staff 1, c" is half note, so that in beats 3 and 4, e' is the upper voice; in staff 3, g is half note, beats 3 and 4 have c quarter notes. Measure 31, staff 1 has no whole note c"; staff 3, upper voice is c whole note. In edition A', measure 27, staff 1, lower voice, beats 1 and 2 have c' dotted quarter note, e', g' sixteenth notes (the two sixteenth notes are beamed with beat 3, note 1—g' eighth note).

In the preface to his edition of the Bach organ works (in the section discussing sudden transitions from *forte* to *piano* and the use of the swell box for accents), Widor gives measures 7–9 of this movement in a figure. There he shows a dynamic scheme somewhat expanded from that given in published editions of the symphony: measure 7, beats 3 and 4 have a crescendo hairpin; measure 8, beat 1 has ***pp***, beats 3 and 4 have a crescendo hairpin; measure 9, beat 1 has ***p***, beat 2 has *cresc.* In the published editions Widor never revised the movement to follow this scheme; whether or not it fairly represents his performance practice or was simply an illustrative example is open to question. The editor has not transmitted these dynamic marks to the score. Nevertheless, they do illustrate an important point. "Every progression demands to be punctuated," writes Widor above the figure. And pointing to measures 8 and 9, he continues, "it is necessary to let the first beat of these measures wait a bit (after the two very slight accents of the swell box) in order to give full value to each of the degrees of the progression."†

CRITICAL NOTES

M. 11, ***pp*** is positioned on the second half of beat 1 in all editions—edition follows *Emend* 3. M. 12, staff 2, lower voice, beats 3–4, note 2 is dotted in all editions—an error. M. 29, staff 1, upper voice, note 2 has no dot in any edition—an error.

V. Toccata

If ever there were a piece in which a composer's entire renown lay, this is it. The popularity of the Toccata with organists and audiences alike is practically unparalleled in the organ repertoire. A toccata in the original sense of the word, this *perpetuum mobile* is a real "touch piece." Brilliant figurations rhythmically punctuated by full chords, grand crescendos, and thundering pedals are all combined in a highly idiomatic work for organ. Widor often makes strong intellectual demands on his auditors, but not here. The musical substance can be reduced to a simple nine-chord progression. Without any learned processes this Toccata gains all of its effect from sheer sonority, bravura, and immediacy. It not only pays homage to Widor's teacher Lemmens, who initiated this style of organ toccata, it also must have served as a model on which Debussy mused when he composed the Toccata in his *Suite: Pour le piano* (publ. 1901). As a young man Debussy had served as piano accompanist for Widor's choral society, Concordia, and he could not have escaped hearing Widor's Toccata, which was under the fingers of nearly every organist. In Debussy's Toccata, the section beginning at measure 78 shares with Widor's Toccata the key of F major, a short-long-short rhythmic ostinato, and a general texture—figuration above, doubling a chordally supported melody below; more specifically, Debussy's music features an uncommon melodic phrase (found in Widor at mm. 27, 28, etc.) that moves from *do* through *ti* and *te* to an upward leap to *mi*.

For the performer, the temptation has always been to play Widor's Toccata too fast, with little regard for articulation and clarity—bywords of Widor's style of playing. As Widor became aware of the resultant detrimental effect of these tendencies, he sought to impose more clarity and shape by applying accents and slurs to what had been a totally staccato piece, by decreasing the metronome mark considerably, and by altering the final dynamic scheme to effect a more climactic peroration. There are five slightly varying versions: A', B/B', C, C'/D, and E. Edition E is the principal source. Reports on the variant readings of the earlier versions—except those concerning tempo and articulation given here—follow the critical notes for edition E below.

---

*André Pirro, *Johann Sebastian Bach: The Organist and His Works for Organ*, trans. W. Goodrich (New York: G. Schirmer, 1902), xvii.

†Widor, preface to *Bach: Oeuvres complètes*, 1:xxiv.

Revisions to the tempo and articulation occurred in three stages. To the Allegro of edition A', edition B added a metronome mark of quarter note equals 118. Edition C introduced the accent marks in measures 1–8, staff 2 (by apparent oversight, mm. 5 and 6, beats 3 and 4, have no accents). *Emend* 3 and edition E changed the metronome mark to quarter note equals 100 and introduced the two-note slurs in measures 1 and 2, staff 1 (*Emend* 2 has slurs in mm. 1–3). See plate 2 for a reproduction of the initial page of the Toccata in *Emend* 3. Although the new articulations are given only in the first few measures, Widor clearly intended that they be maintained throughout the piece, as is evidenced by his famous recording of the work;* for J. Hamelle to reengrave the entire movement to reflect these alterations would have been an unnecessary labor and expense. The present edition tacitly carries these patterns of articulation (slurs and accents) to the end. All othereditorial additions appear in accordance with the general editorial policies outlined in this Introduction.

Widor is imprecise as to how the two grand decrescendos and crescendos of this Toccata are to be effected, knowing that each organist must find the smoothest transition on the particular instrument at hand. To that end, he only offers a few dynamic marks as well as *cresc.* and *diminuendo* directives. After the manual change to **R** (m. 33), the dynamic marks in measures 47–49 may be interpreted as follows: measure 47 (*f*)—swell box fully open; measure 48 (*ff*)—**PR** with Anches; measure 49 (*fff*)—**GPR** and Pédale with Anches. Widor had a superior solution to this, however, and if possible it should be followed. Clarence Eddy reported observing Widor play this movement (until m. 66, where the left hand moves to **PR**) solely on the Grand Choeur (the coupler keyboard).†

> He reduces the organ and builds it up again in the most wonderful way; it cannot be done so successfully upon any other organ. There are an immense number of mechanical contrivances, quite original in design. He combines all the different manuals (five manuals the organ has, the great organ being lowest of all) by means of pedals, which bring on or throw off the couplers [and Jeux de combinaison]. He can reduce the organ to almost nothing without taking his hands from the keys and builds [*sic*] it up again without interrupting the voice flow in any respect. He makes a *diminuendo* which is something extraordinary in that church, and a *crescendo* which will simply lift you off your feet.‡

To do this, of course, requires not only silencing the **G** Anches, but the Fonds as well; then, by uncoupling **P**, **R** alone will remain on the **G** manual.

As with the preceding movement, Widor gives an example from this one (mm. 40–41) in the preface to his edition of the Bach organ works (in the section discussing sudden transitions from forte to piano). Here again the dynamic scheme is slightly altered from that in the published symphony: measure 40, beat 1 has *sempre cresc.*, beat 4 has no decrescendo hairpin; measure 41, beat 1 has ***pp***. Concerning this, he writes:

> As after full sunlight a little time is needed to get used to shade, so the ear needs a little space between a *forte* and a *piano*. If we pass suddenly from the *forte* of the Grand orgue to the *piano* of the Récit, if we leap from high to low, we should wait as the sound dies away to go up to the Récit or to descend to the low octaves. By going on metronomically, straight ahead, without regard to resonance, the end of the first-manual phrase will smother the beginning of the other; all will entangle in a porridge without color and without taste. The public will not be conscious of this liberty taken with the regularity of the time, this necessary respiration; . . . After the crescendo of measure 40 it will be impossible to perceive the pianissimo of measure 41, that is to say the change of dynamic, if one does not breathe boldly before attacking the chord on g-sharp in staff 2. Now, no one will notice this breath, as long as it is natural; you are not playing in time since you insert an extra value before measure 41, but you keep the rhythm, and that is enough for the listener.§

CRITICAL NOTES

M. 23, staff 3, beat 4, note is staccato in all editions—this is apparently an engraver's error (the notes in mm. 24–26 are not marked staccato); Widor, in fact, holds these notes quite long on his recording,‖ and *Riem*5 has them so marked.# M. 42, staff 2, upper voice, dyads 1–4 have no articulation marks in any edition—an error. M. 47, staff 1, beat 2, note 4 has no staccato dot in any edition—an error. M. 49, staves 1 and 2, in accord with Widor's practice (stated in par. 9 of his *Avant-propos*) ***fff*** signals the arrival of full organ, consequently the return to **GPR**.

M. 52, staff 2, beat 4, upper voice, triad 3 has no staccato dot in any edition—an error. M. 58, staff 1 has *sempre staccato* in all editions—at this point, except in m. 62, Widor stopped marking staccato dots for the sixteenth-note figurations until m. 71. M. 64, staff 2, beat 4, the f′ in the dyad f/f′ is very lightly struck through in red pencil in *Emend* 3—this does not appear to mark a definitive decision (other alterations are marked in ink and blue pencil, often with daggers; see pl. 2); because of the vagueness of this strikethrough and because the deletion of the note may only make the passage slightly easier to play, the note has not been

---

Orgues et organistes français en 1930, EMI 2 C 153-16411/5.

†For a description of technical aspects of the Saint-Sulpice organ together with its specification, see Performance Guidelines in the Preface to this edition (vol. 11, Symphonie I, xxi–xxiv.

‡Clarence Eddy, "Great Frenchmen of Organ World in 1897 Are Pictured by Eddy," reprinted in *Diapason* 28 (May 1937): 14.

§Widor, preface to *Bach: Oeuvres complètes*, 1:xxiv.

‖The following observations illustrate a few of the liberties Widor took while recording on that April evening in 1932. In the passage under consideration (mm. 23–30), Widor played the staff-3 notes with approximately the following values: Mm. 23–25, notes are half notes. M. 26, note 1 is whole note. M. 27, note 1 is slightly long whole note. M. 28, note 1 is dotted whole note. M. 29, notes 1 and 3 are double-dotted half notes. M. 30, note is dotted half note.

#In *Riem*5, staff 3, mm. 23 and 25, a slur is drawn from the quarter note under the subsequent quarter rest; in mm. 24 and 26 the quarter note on the downbeat is circled (enlarged) in such a way as to suggest that a half note might be played. In short, it appears in *Riem*5 as if Widor wanted to replicate the note values of mm. 26–27, 27–28, and 28–29 in mm. 23–24 and 25–26—and while this was never carried out in any published version, it is consistent with the composer's own recorded performance.

deleted from the present edition; the dyad has no staccato dot in any edition—an error. M. 66, staff 2, beat 4, last note (c''') has no staccato dot in any edition—an error. M. 67, staff 1, the manual directive is **G** in all editions—this is certainly an abbreviated directive (for **GPR**) given as a cautionary after the change of manual for the left hand.

M. 71, beat 1, the editorial *p* marks follow *Emend* 2. M. 74, *cresc.* is introduced in *Emend* 3 and edition *E;* the editorial manual directive follows all previous editions, where **G** is given as an abbreviation at beat 2.

Version *C'/D* differs from edition *E* as follows (see paragraph on tempo and articulation in the Critical Commentary for changes in these elements). M. 68 has no *sempre diminuendo*. M. 74, staves 1 and 2, beat 2, have **G{** in lieu of *cresc.*

Edition *C* differs from version *C'/D* as follows. M. 28, staff 3, beat 4 is b-natural quarter note, quarter rest. M. 66, staff 1, beat 1, note 6 is c''-sharp in *Emend* 1 (by analogy, m. 70, note 6 would be c'-sharp)—this contemplated change was never effected. M. 70, staff 3, note 2 is F in *Emend* 1. M. 71, staff 3, note 1 is f in *Emend* 1; staves 2 and 3, beat 3, the staccatos are crossed out and tenuto dashes are inserted in *Emend* 1—perhaps by oversight Widor neglected to make this emendation on beat 1 when he revised the staff-3 note. M. 72, staves 2 and 3, beat 1, the staccatos are crossed out and tenuto dashes are inserted in *Emend* 1.

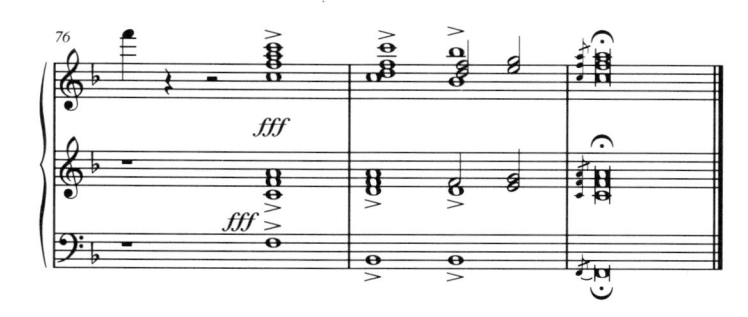

Example 2. V. Toccata, mm. 76–78, in editions *A'* through *B'*.

Version *B/B'* differs from edition *C* as follows (see paragraph on tempo and articulation in the Critical Commentary for changes in these elements). M. 65 has no *diminuendo*. M. 73 has no *cresc.* Mm. 76–78 appear in example 2.

Edition *A'* differs from version *B/B'* as follows. There is no metronome mark. M. 50 has no *maestoso*. M. 69, staff 1, beats 1 and 2, note 6 is b[-flat]; beat 3, note 6 is a. M. 70, staff 3, note 1 is whole note (beat 2 has no half rest). M. 75, staff 2, notes 1–3 are c'', a', c''.

Widor's *Avant-propos*

Although it may not be customary to place a preface at the front of musical editions, I believe it is necessary to put one here in order to explain the character, the style, the procedures of registration, and the sign conventions of these eight symphonies.

Old instruments had almost no reed stops: two colors, white and black, foundation stops and mixture stops—that was their entire palette; moreover, each transition between this white and this black was abrupt and rough; the means of graduating the body of sound did not exist. Consequently, Bach and his contemporaries deemed it pointless to indicate registrations for their works—the mixture stops traditionally remaining appropriate to rapid movements, and the foundation stops to pieces of a more solemn pace.

The invention of the "swell box" dates back to just before the end of the eighteenth century. In a work published in 1772, the Dutchman Hess de Gouda expresses the admiration he felt upon hearing Handel, in London, coming to grips with the new device; some time later, in 1780, Abbé Vogler recommends the use of the "box" in the German manufacture of instruments. The idea gained ground, but without great artistic effect—for in spite of the most perspicacious efforts, they did not succeed in going beyond the limits of a thirty-key manual and an insignificant number of registers.

It was necessary to wait until 1839 for the solution to the problem.

The honor for it redounds to French industry and the glory to Mr. A. Cavaillé-Coll. It is he who conceived the diverse wind pressures, the divided windchests, the pedal systems and the combination registers, he who applied for the first time Barker's pneumatic motors, created the family of harmonic stops, reformed and perfected the mechanics to such a point that each pipe—low or high, loud or soft—instantly obeys the touch of the finger, the keys becoming as light as those of a piano—the resistances being suppressed, rendering the combination of [all] the forces of the instrument practical. From this result: the possibility of confining an entire division in a sonorous prison—opened or closed at will—the freedom of mixing timbres, the means of intensifying them or gradually tempering them, the freedom of tempos, the sureness of attacks, the balance of contrasts, and, finally, a whole blossoming of wonderful colors—a rich palette of the most diverse shades: harmonic flutes, gambas, bassoons, English horns, trumpets, celestes, flue stops and reed stops of a quality and variety unknown before.

The modern organ is essentially symphonic. The new instrument requires a new language, an ideal other than scholastic polyphony. It is no longer the Bach of the fugue whom we invoke but the heartrending melodist, the preeminently expressive master of the Preludes, the Magnificat, the B-minor Mass, the cantatas, and the *St. Matthew Passion*.

But this "expressiveness" of the new instrument can only be subjective; it arises from mechanical means and cannot have spontaneity. While the stringed and wind instruments of the orchestra, the piano, and voices reign only by naturalness of accent and unexpectedness of attack, the organ, clothed in its primordial majesty, speaks as a philosopher: alone among all, it can put forth the same volume of sound indefinitely and thus inspire the religious idea of the infinite. Surprises and accents are not natural to it; they are lent to it, they are accents by adoption. It is clear that their use requires tact and discernment. It is also clear to what extent the organ symphony differs from the orchestral symphony. No confusion is to be feared. One will never write indiscriminately for the orchestra or for the organ, but henceforth one will have to exercise the same care with the combination of timbres in an organ composition as in an orchestral work.

Rhythm itself must come under the influence of modern trends: it must lend itself to a sort of elasticity of the measure, all the while preserving its rights. It must allow the musical phrase to punctuate its paragraphs and breathe when necessary, provided that it hold [the phrase] by the bit and that [the phrase] march to its step. Without rhythm, without this constant manifestation of the will returning periodically to the strong beat, the performer will not be listened to. How often the composer hesitates and abstains at the moment of writing on his score the *poco ritenuto* that he has in his thought! He does not dare, from fear that the exaggeration of the performer may weaken or break the flow of the piece. The indication is left out. We do not have the graphic means for emphasizing the end of a period, or reinforcing a chord by a type of pause of unnoticeable duration. Isn't it a great shame, especially since the organ is an instrument that draws all of its effect from time values?

As to terminology, the system indicating the disposition of timbres—usage having established nothing as yet—it seemed practical to me to note the manual and pedal registration at the head of each piece; to apportion by tone colors, rather than an exact nomenclature of stops, the intensity of the sonorities of the same family; to designate the manuals by their abbreviations (two or more initials juxtaposed signifying the coupling of two or more manuals); to assume the reed stops always prepared; and finally to reserve *fff* for the full power of the organ, without having to mention the introduction of the ventil (Anches) pedals. In the combination **GR**

[Grand-orgue, Récit], the crescendo applies only to the Récit, unless this crescendo leads to the *fff*, in which case all the forces of the instrument must enter little by little in order, flues and reeds.

It is unnecessary, I believe, to implore the same precision, the same coordination of the feet and hands in leaving a keyboard as in attacking it, and to protest against all carrying-over of the pedal after the time, an old-fashioned custom that has happily almost disappeared.

With the consummate musicians of today, the insufficiencies and shortcomings in musical notation become less worrisome; the composer is more certain of seeing his intentions understood and his implications perceived. Between him and the performer is a steadfast collaboration, which the growing number of virtuosos will render more intimate and fruitful every day.

Ch. M. W.

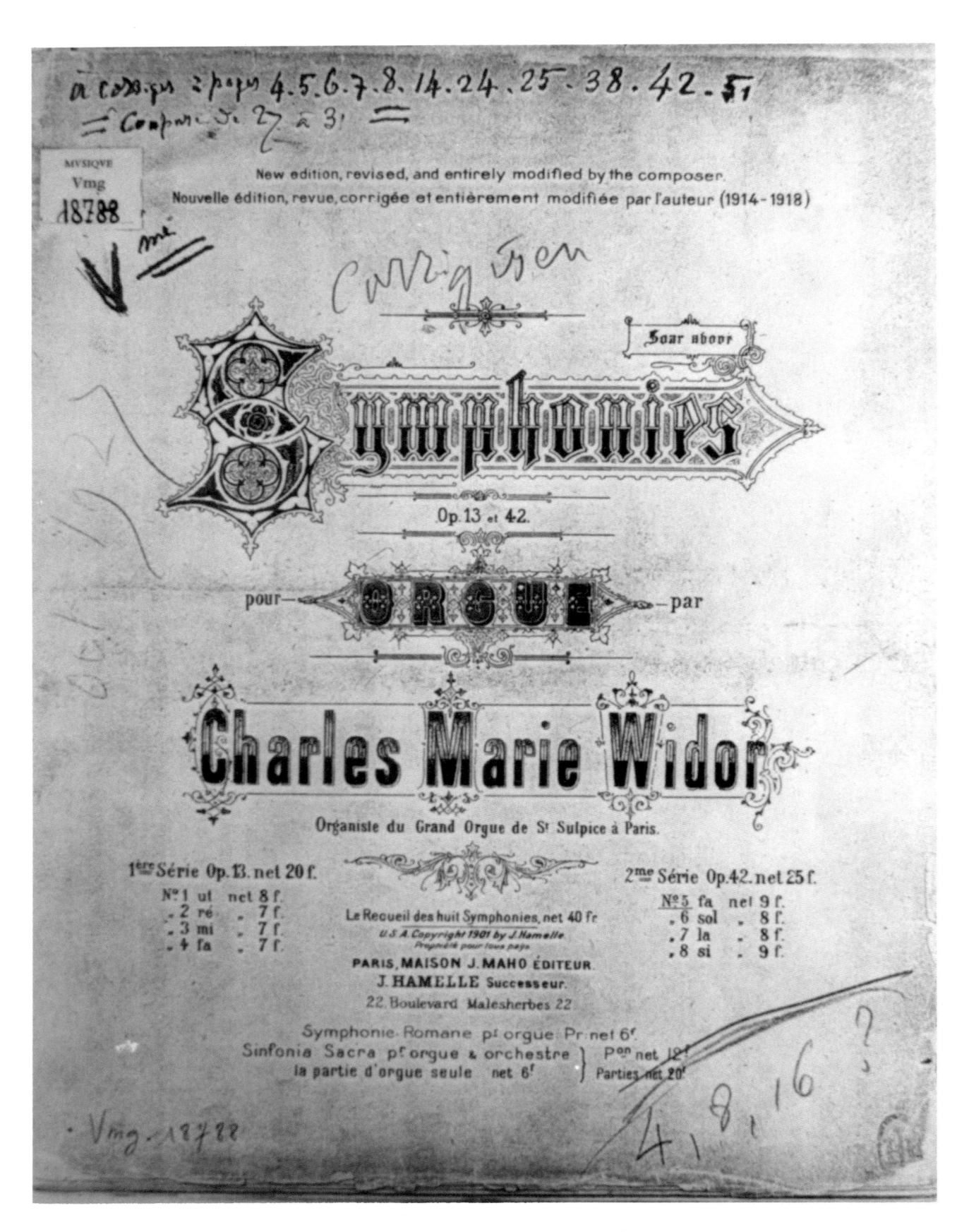

Plate 1. Cover to *Emend* 3. It has been argued in the Preface to this edition (vol. 11, Symphonie I, "Autograph Revisions") that *Emend* 3 (an emended copy of edition *D*) is a source very close to the *Stichvorlage* for edition *E*. On its cover Widor listed the pages where he had made corrections and a cut, presumably in preparation for the new edition (the first page of music in *Emend* 3 is numbered 3). The fact that there are other emendations, found on pages not listed and not appearing in edition *E*, suggests that Widor continued to refine this score after the October 1927 date written along the left side.
Courtesy Bibliothèque nationale, Paris

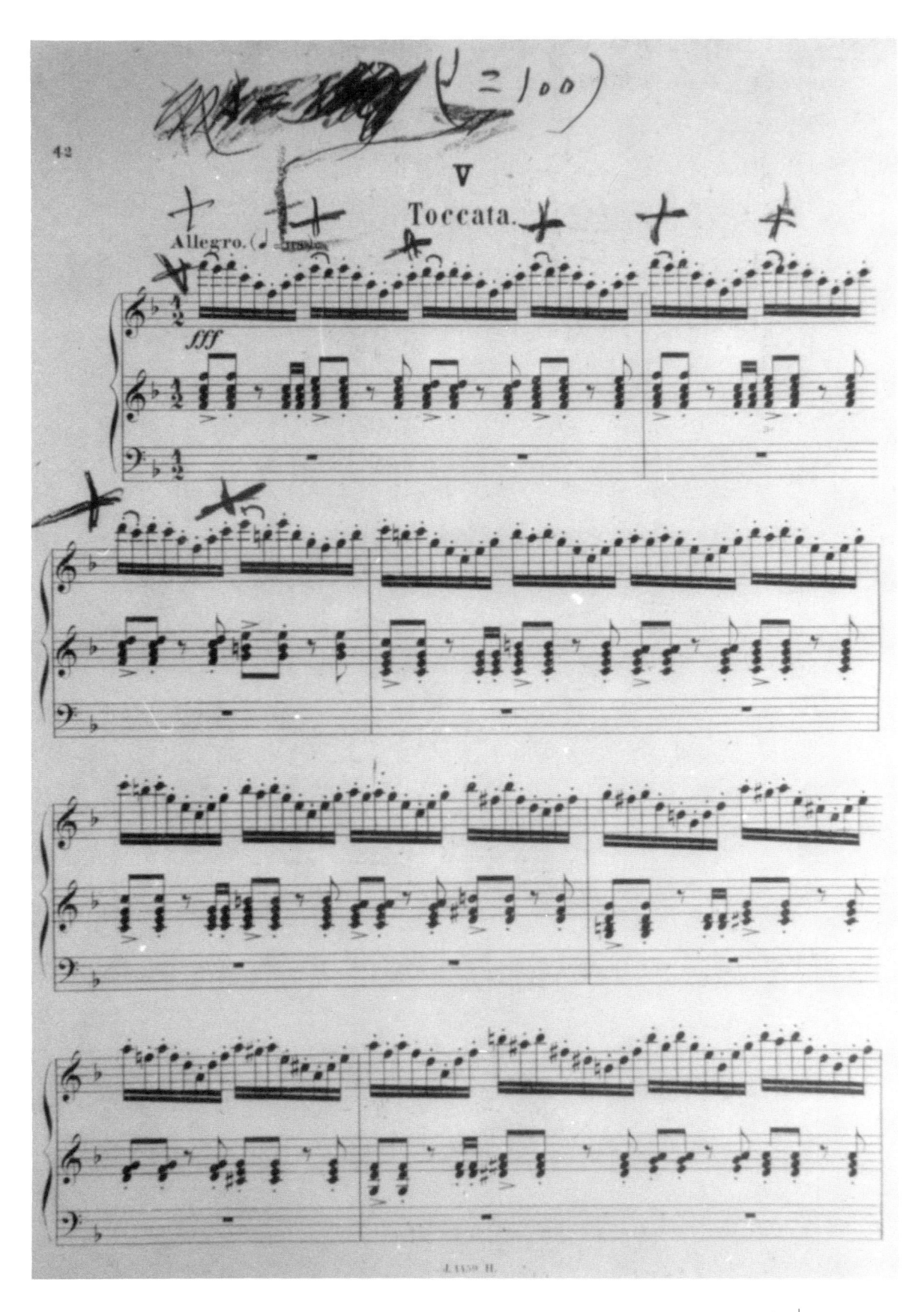

Plate 2. Toccata, page 42 of *Emend* 3. Widor first considered a metronome mark ($\quarternote = 108$), which can be discerned through the cross out in the original.
Courtesy Bibliothèque nationale, Paris

Symphonie V in F Minor

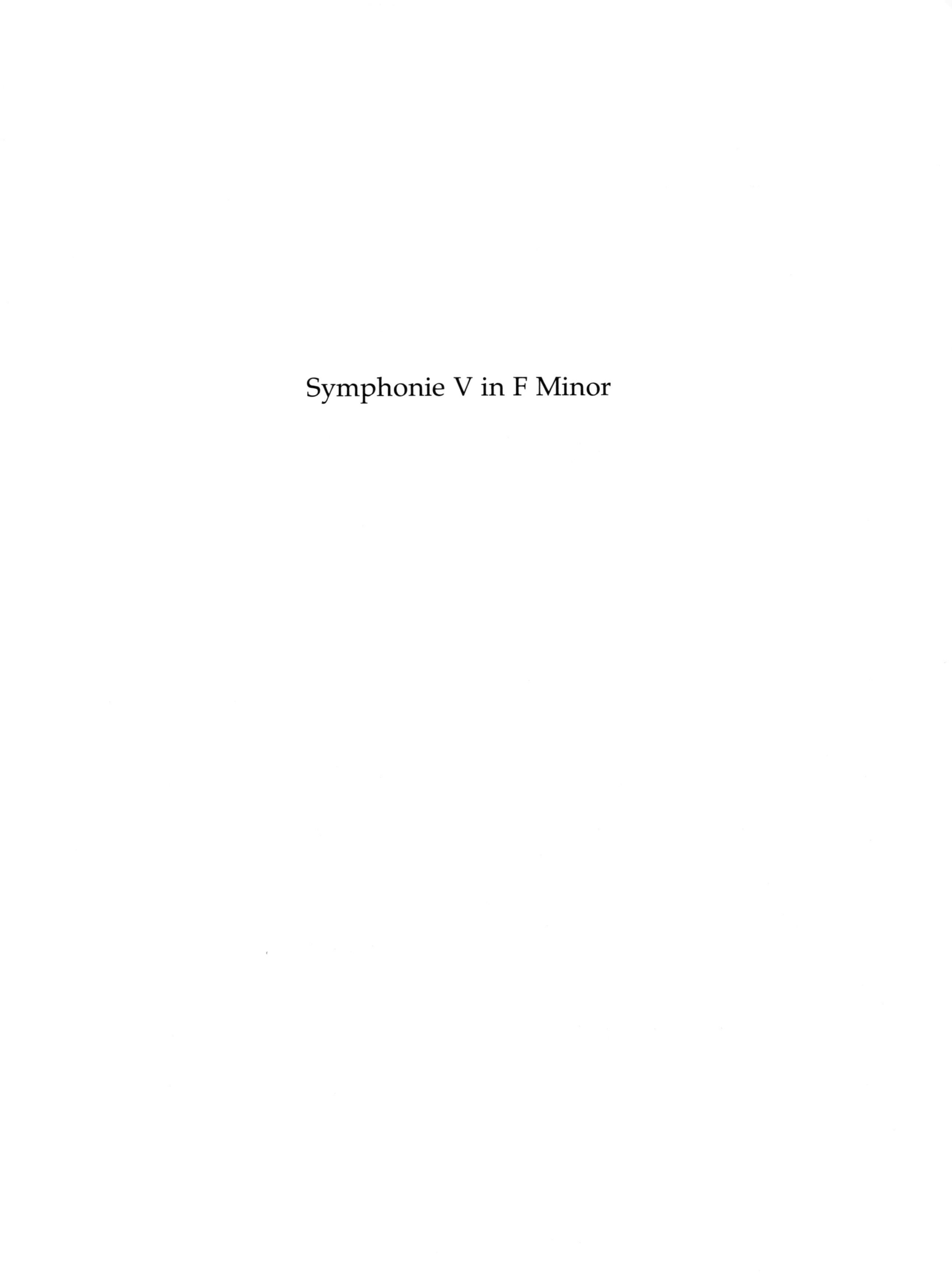

Grand orgue: Fonds 16', 8', 4'
Positif: Montres et Gambes 8'
Récit: Flûtes 16', 4', Hautbois [8']
Pédale: Basses 16', 8'

I

Allegro vivace ($\natural = 69$)

24
R
30
GR
35
riten.
a tempo
1.
R
GR
41
R Flûtes 8', 4'
2.
R
(Péd. Flûte 8' solo)

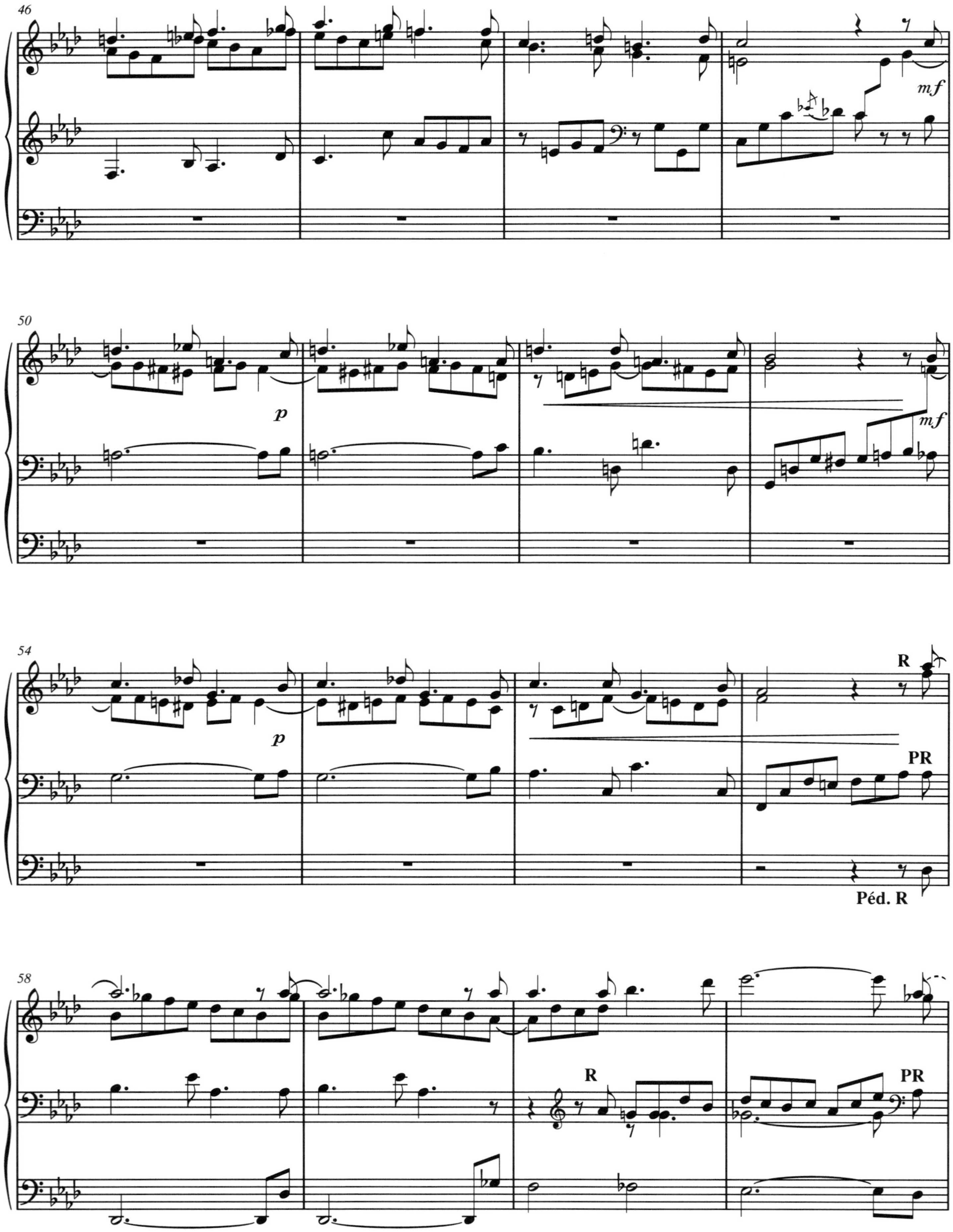
46
mf
50
p
mf
54
p
R
PR
Péd. R
58
R
PR

62
rit.
a tempo
R
67
71
Adagio
Tempo I
[R] Anches 16', 8', 4'
rit.
mf
f
Péd. GR Fonds 16', 8', 4'
75
R

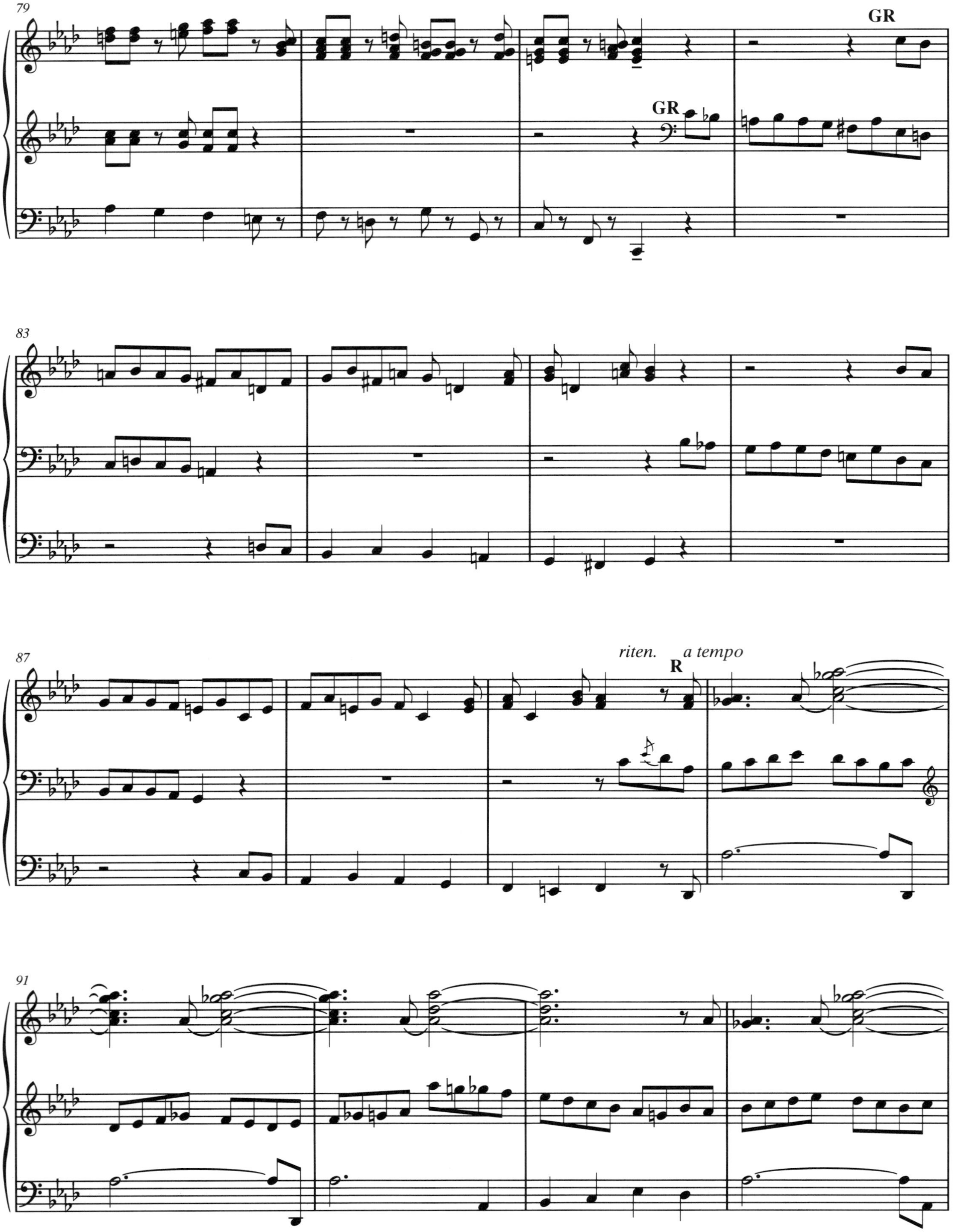
79
GR
GR
83
87
riten.
R
a tempo
91

a piacere
a tempo
95
p
99
R
103
G
(Péd. Flûte 8' solo)
riten.
a tempo
108

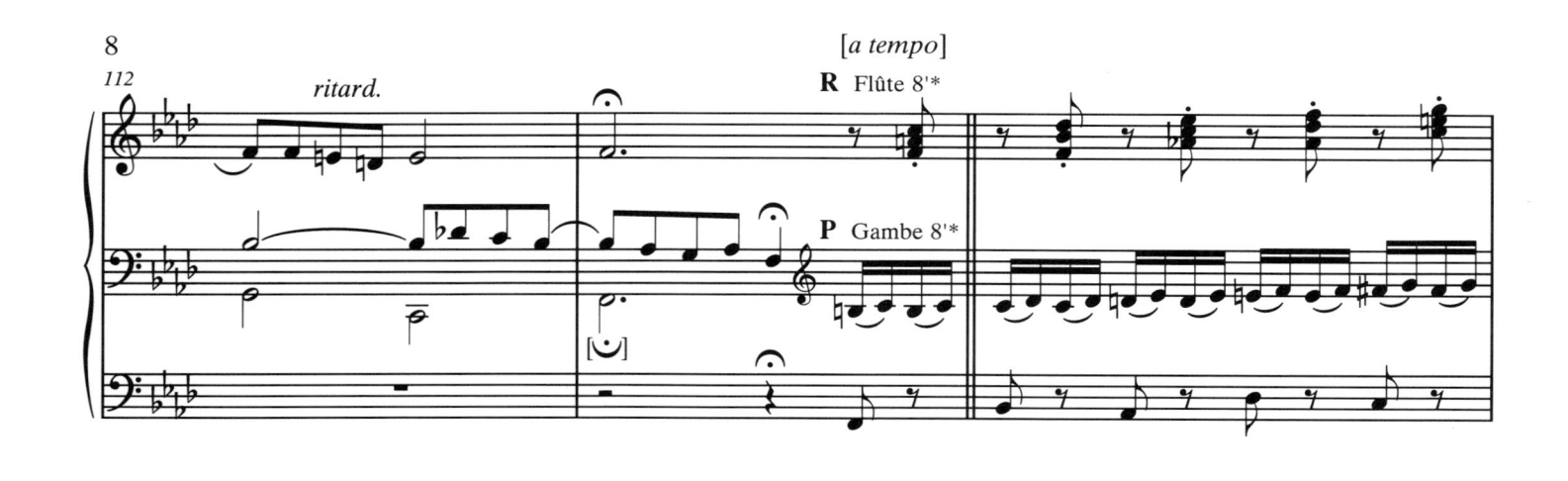

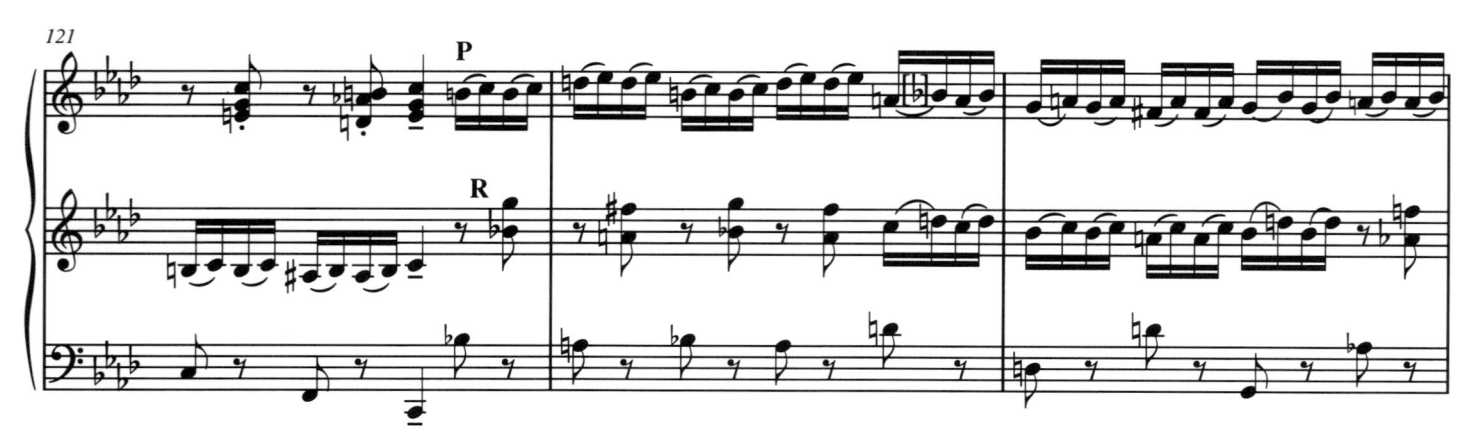

*See Critical Notes.

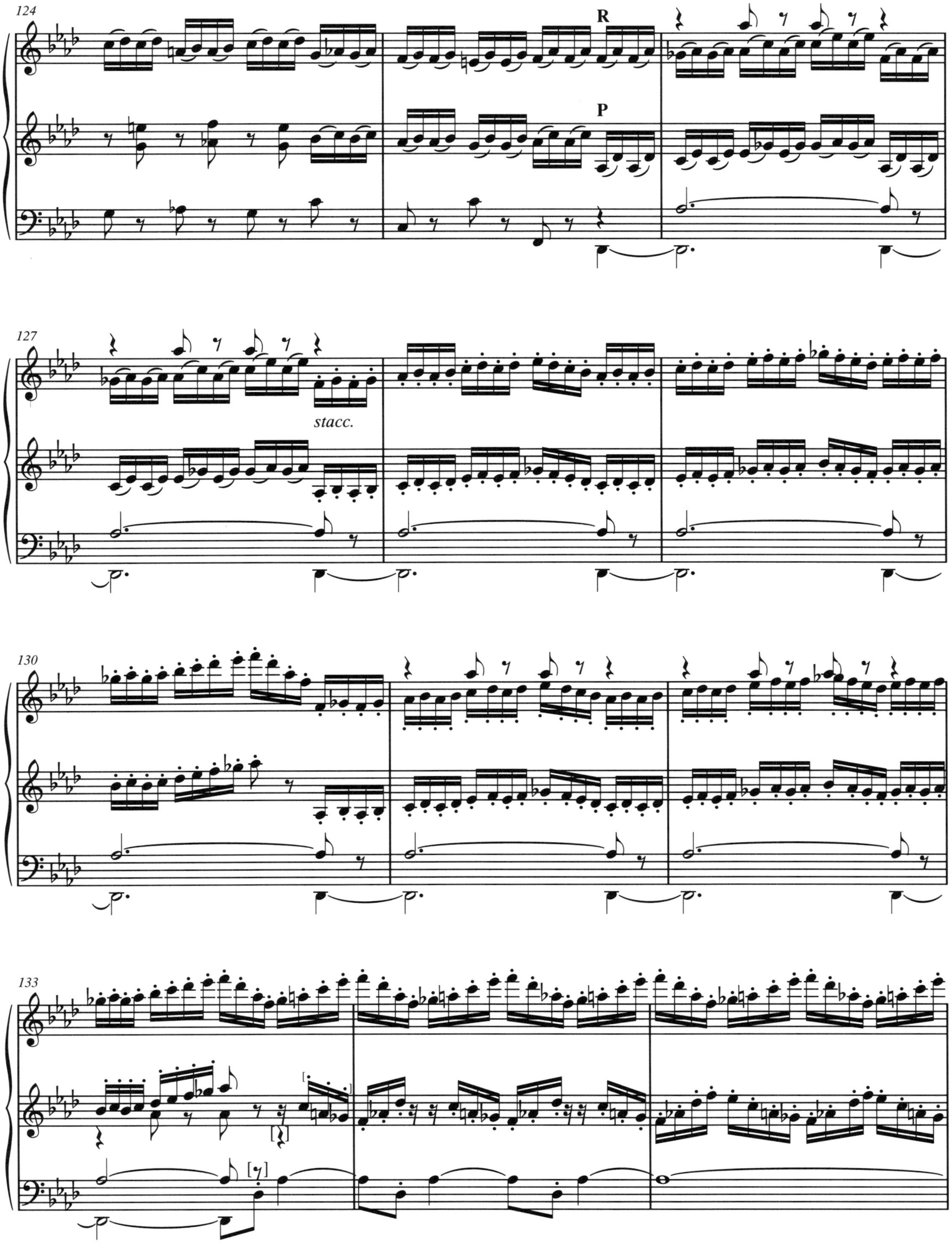
124
R
P
127
stacc.
130
133

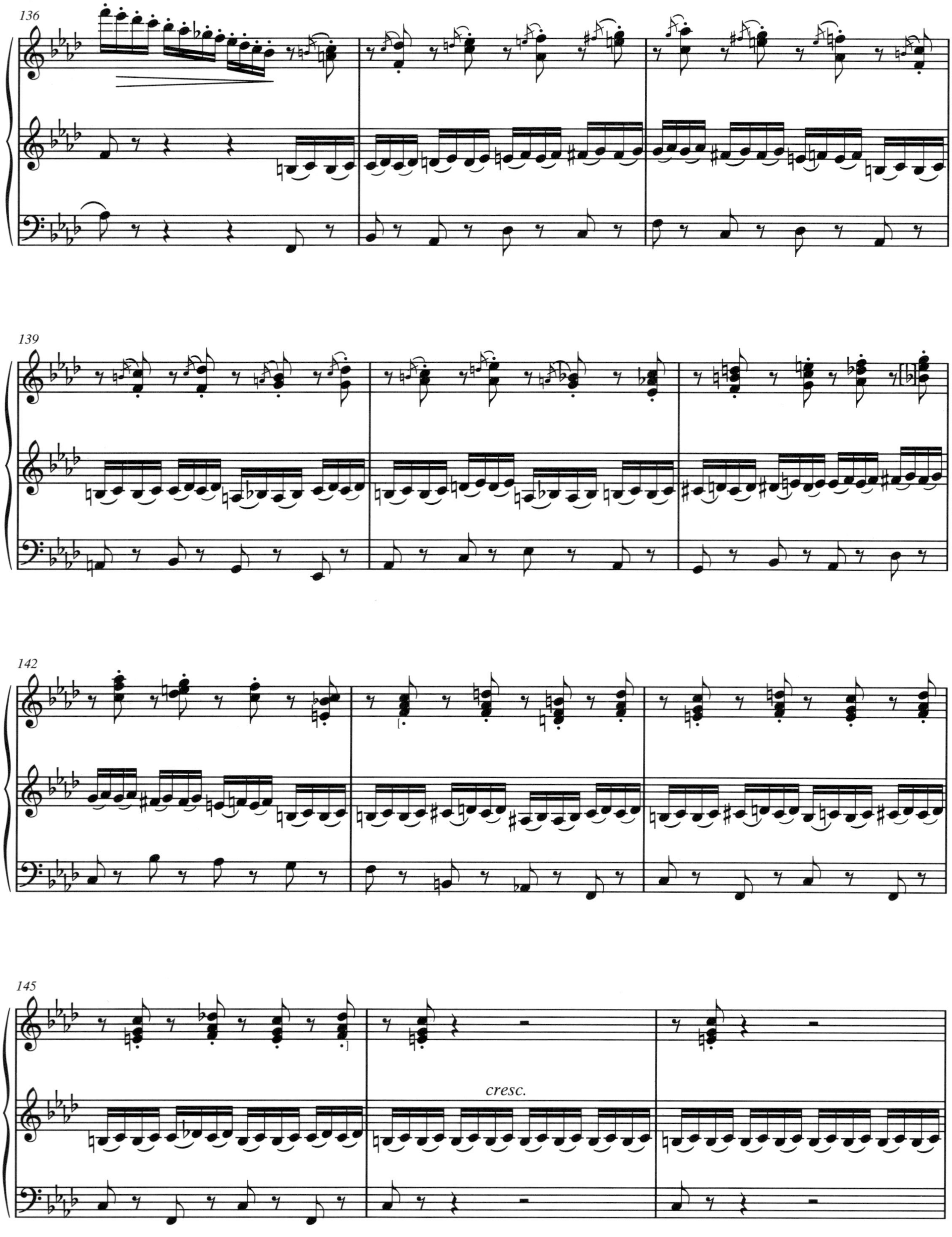
136
139
142
145
cresc.

Più lento
GPR Fonds 8', 4'
148
[P]
cresc.
GPR
f
Péd. G[PR] Fonds 16', 8', 4'
f
152
158
163
PR
G[PR]
f

169
174
poco ritard.
PR
rit.
179
Scherzando (♩ = 96)
R Fonds 8', 4', Hautbois
R
pp
183
R Anches 16', 8', 4'
pp
Péd. solo

187
191
R
pp
G Fonds 16', 8', 4'
GR
Péd. GR
194
agitato
GR
R
196
198
agitato
GR
R

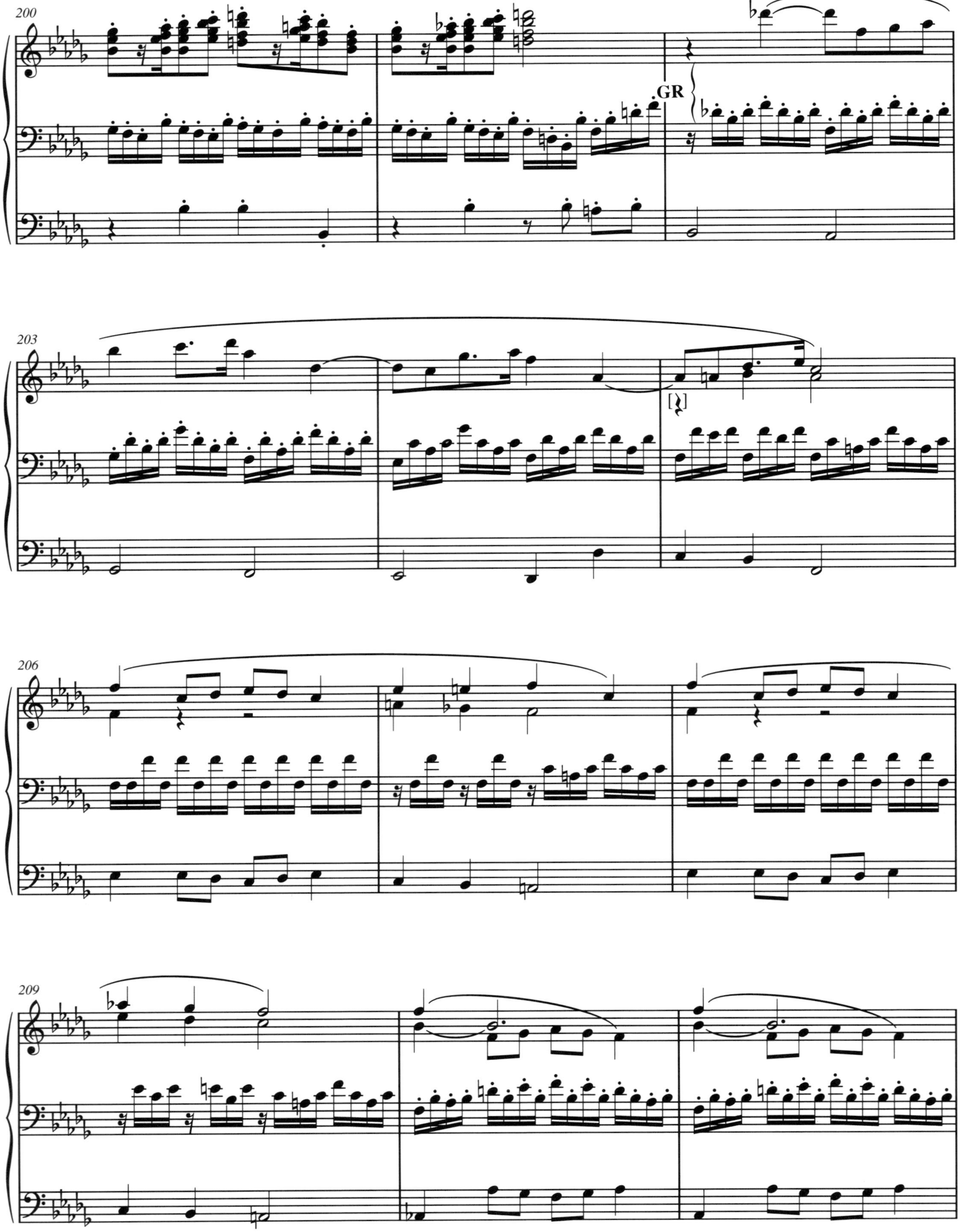
200
GR
203
206
209

15

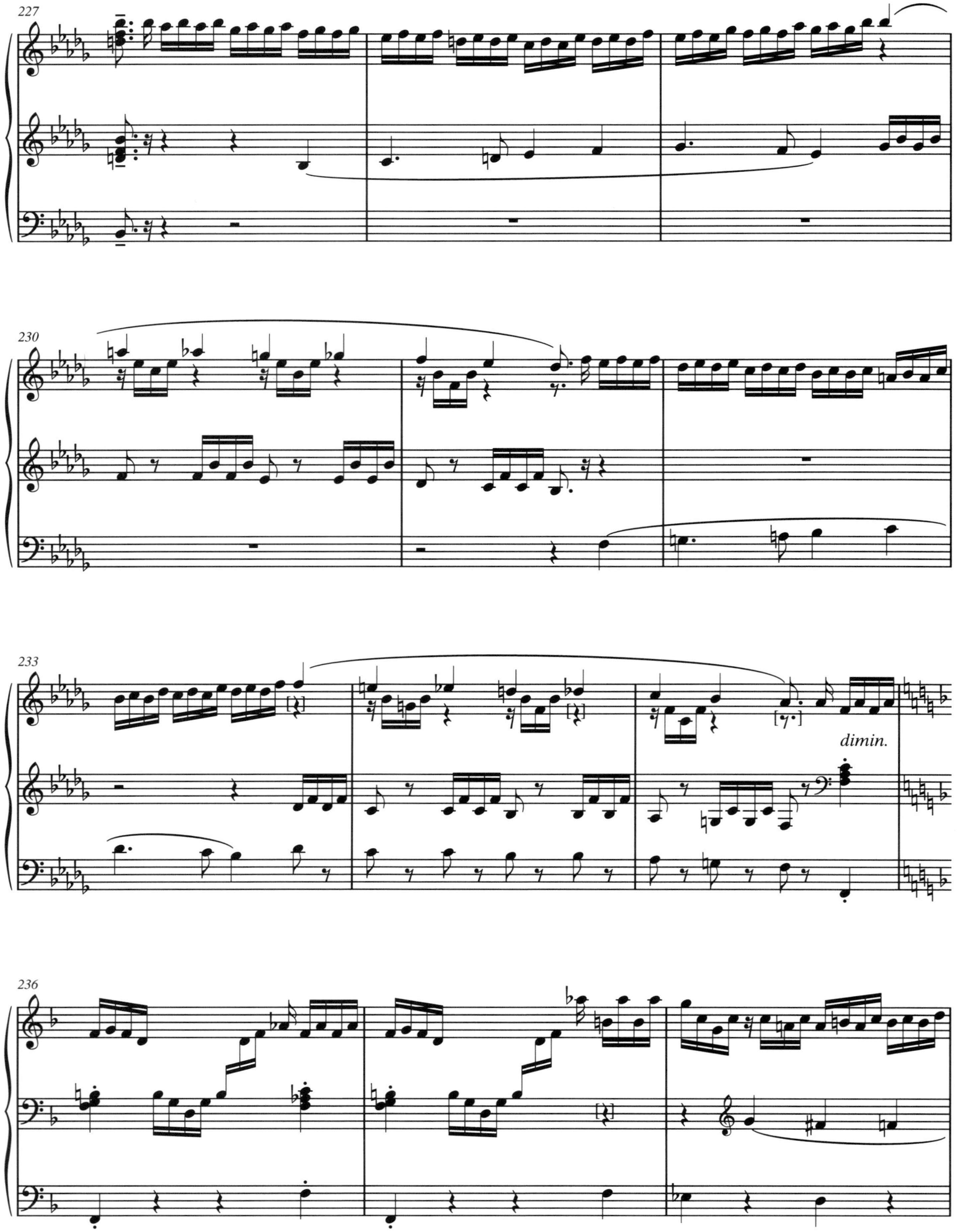
227
230
233
dimin.
236

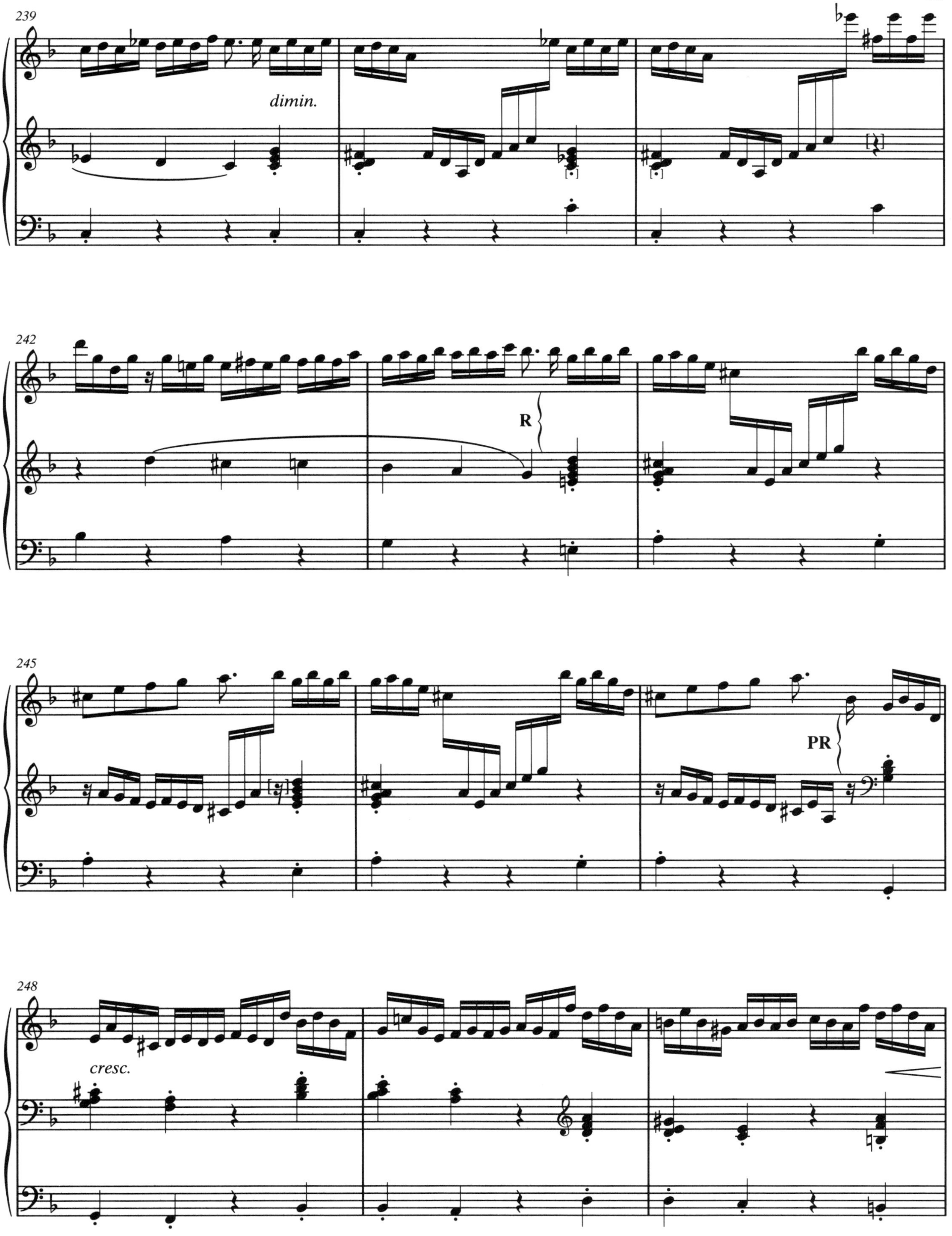
239
dimin.
242
R
245
PR
248
cresc.

18

269
sf sf sf sf sf
275
sf mf
mf
cre - scen - do
280
rit.
a tempo
286
rit.
fff
fff

This page has been left blank to facilitate page turns.

Grand orgue: Flûte 8'
Positif: Flûtes 8', 4'
Récit: Hautbois [8']
Pédale: Basses 16', 8'

II

Allegro cantabile

a piacere, moderato

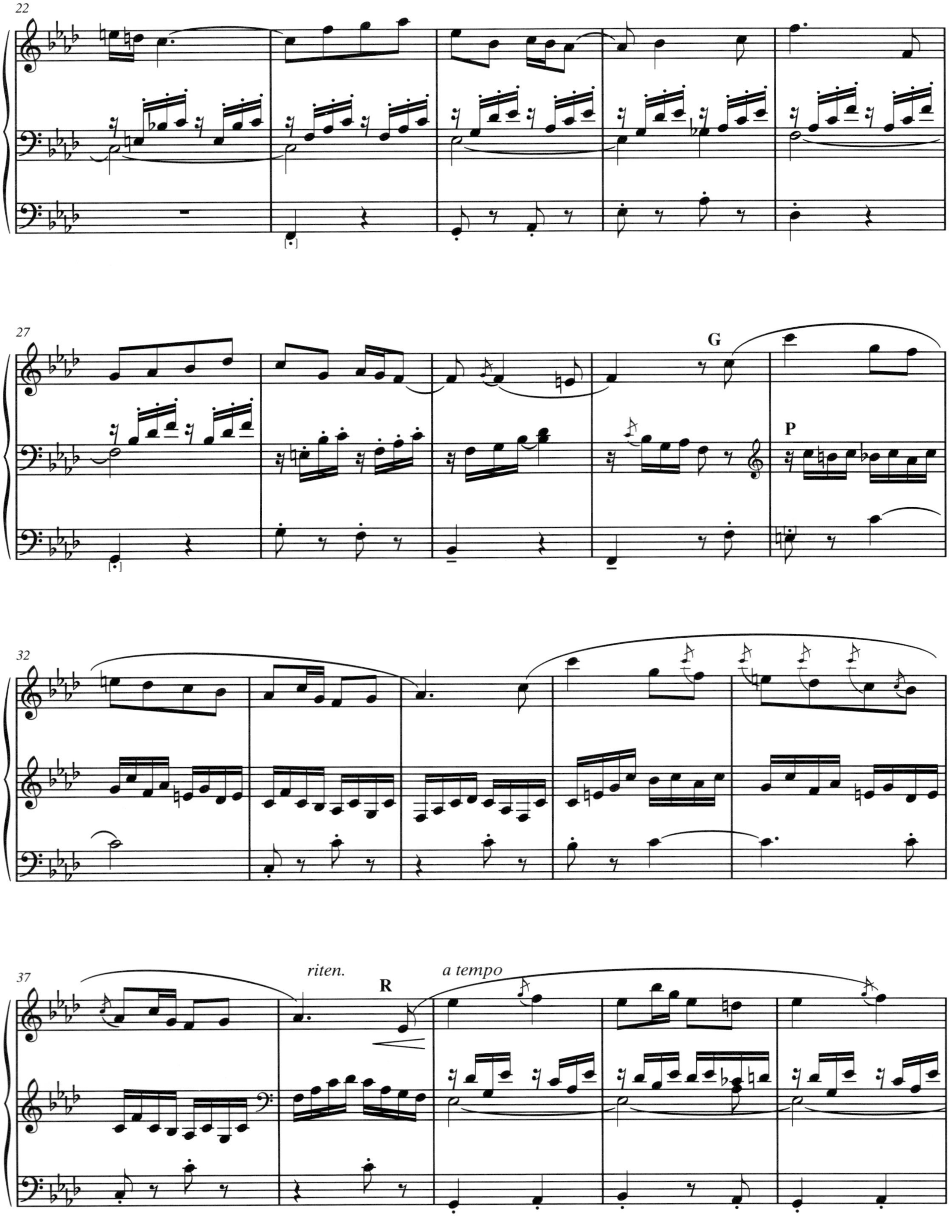
22
27
G
P
32
37
riten.
R
a tempo

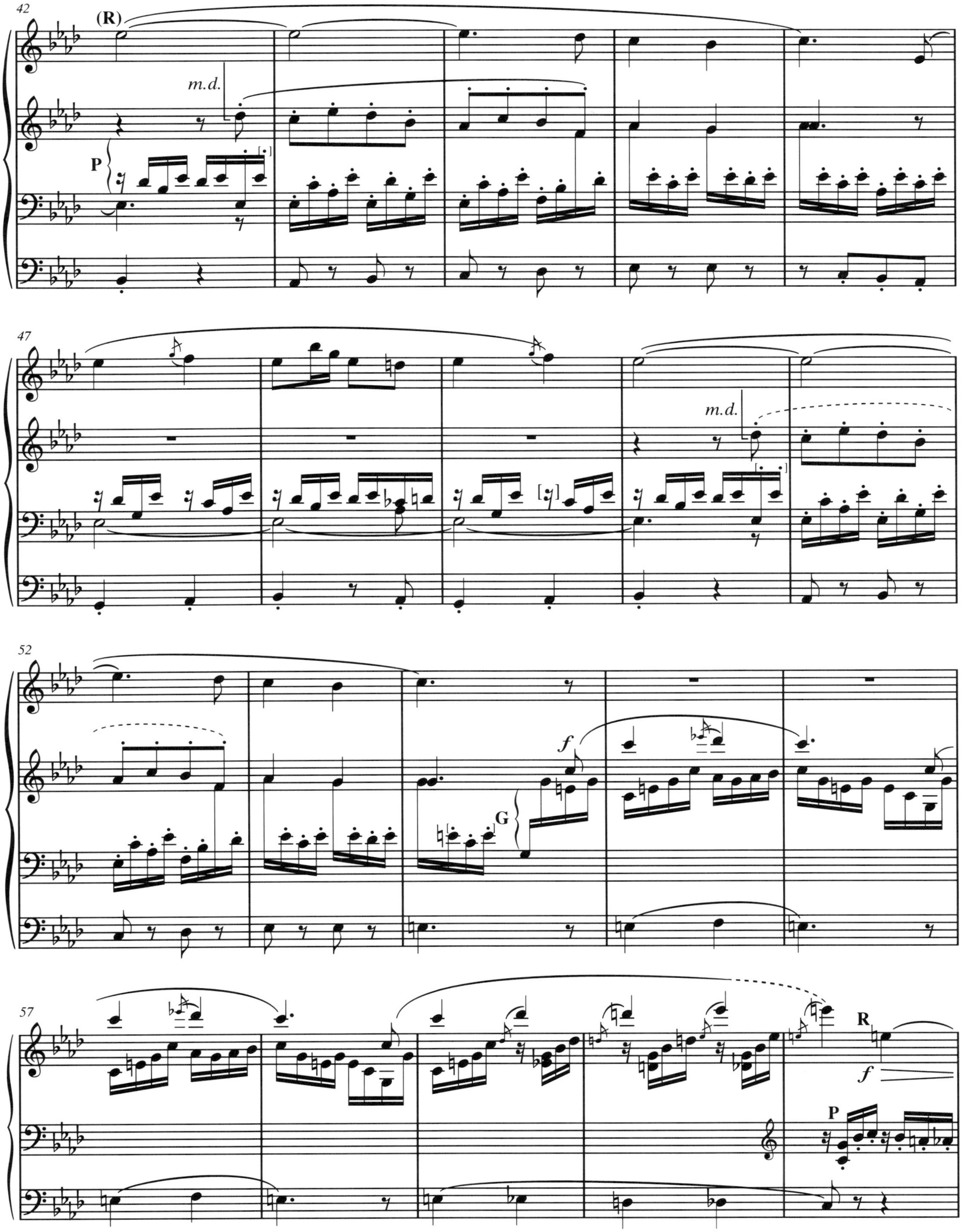
42
(R)
m.d.
P
47
m.d.
52
f
G
57
R
f
P

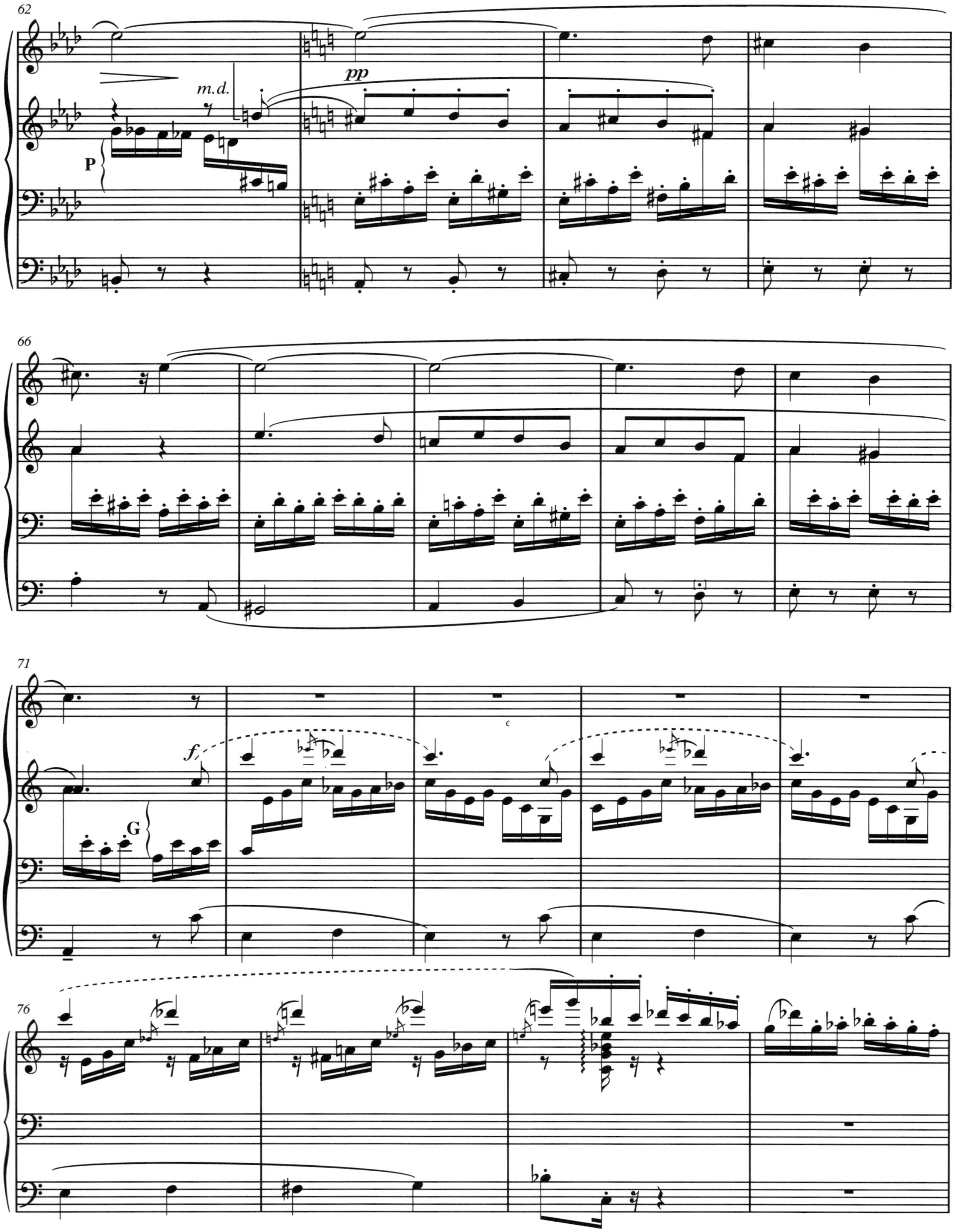
62
m.d.
pp
P
66
71
f
G
76

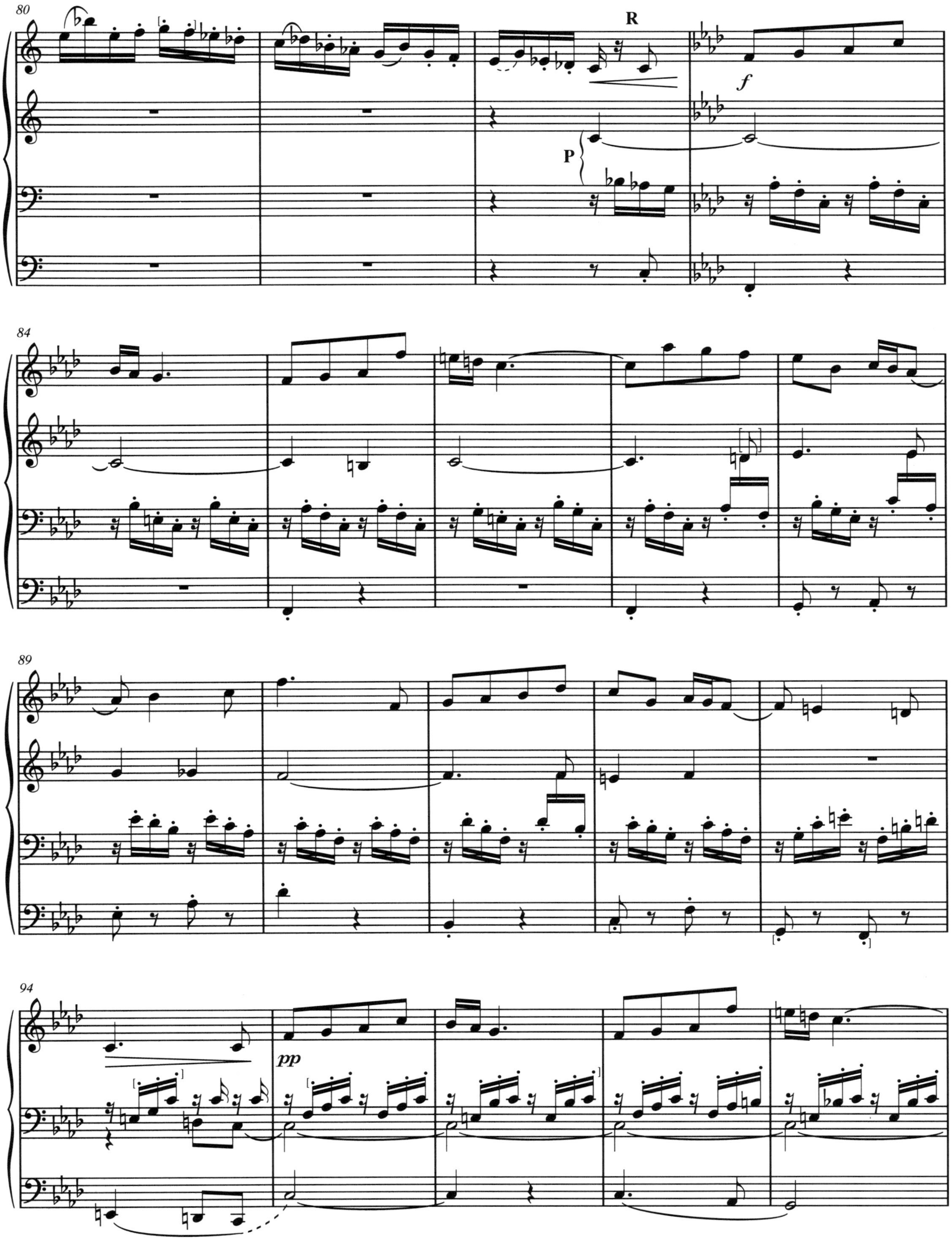
80
R
f
P
84
89
94
pp

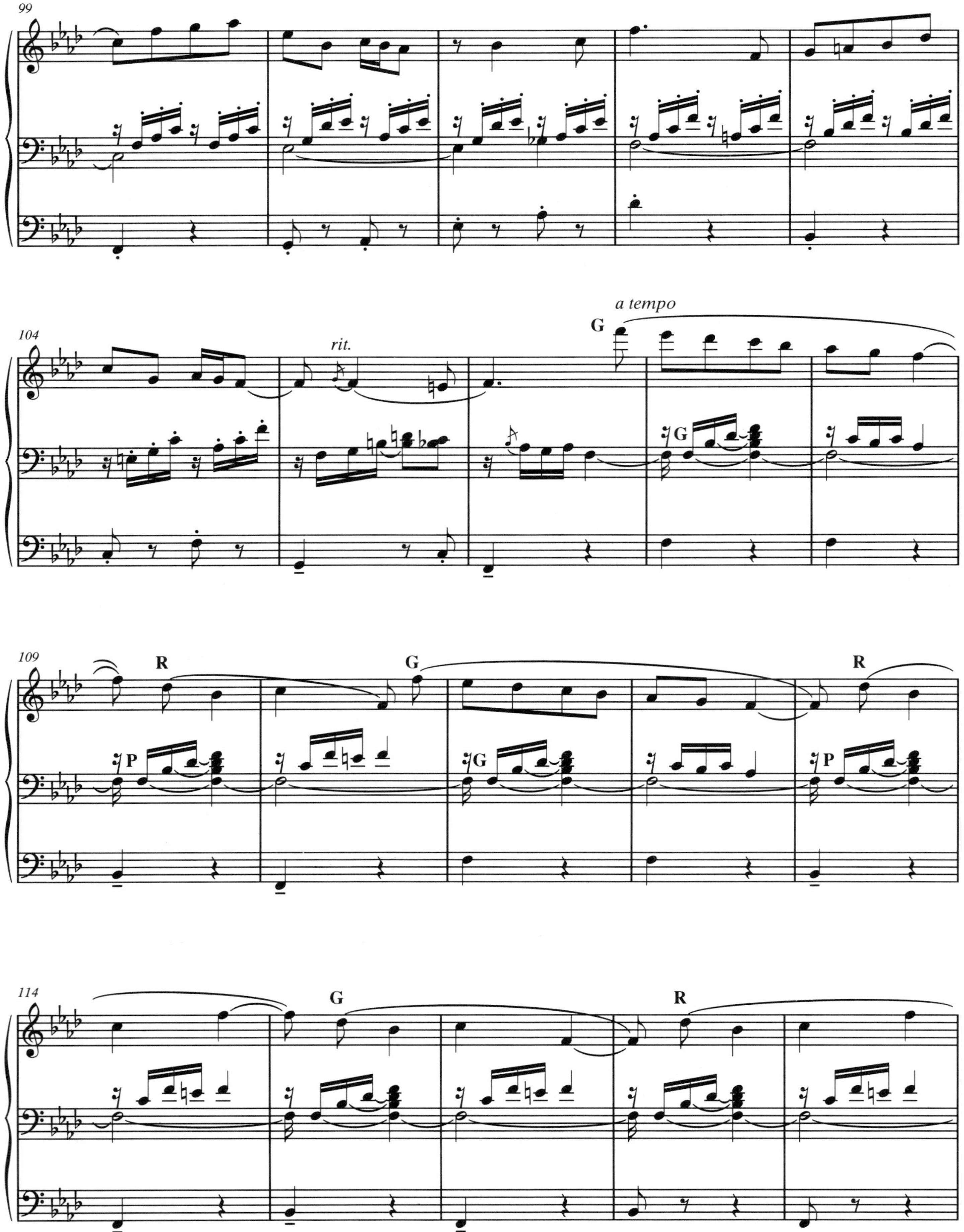
99
104
rit.
a tempo
G
P
109
R
114

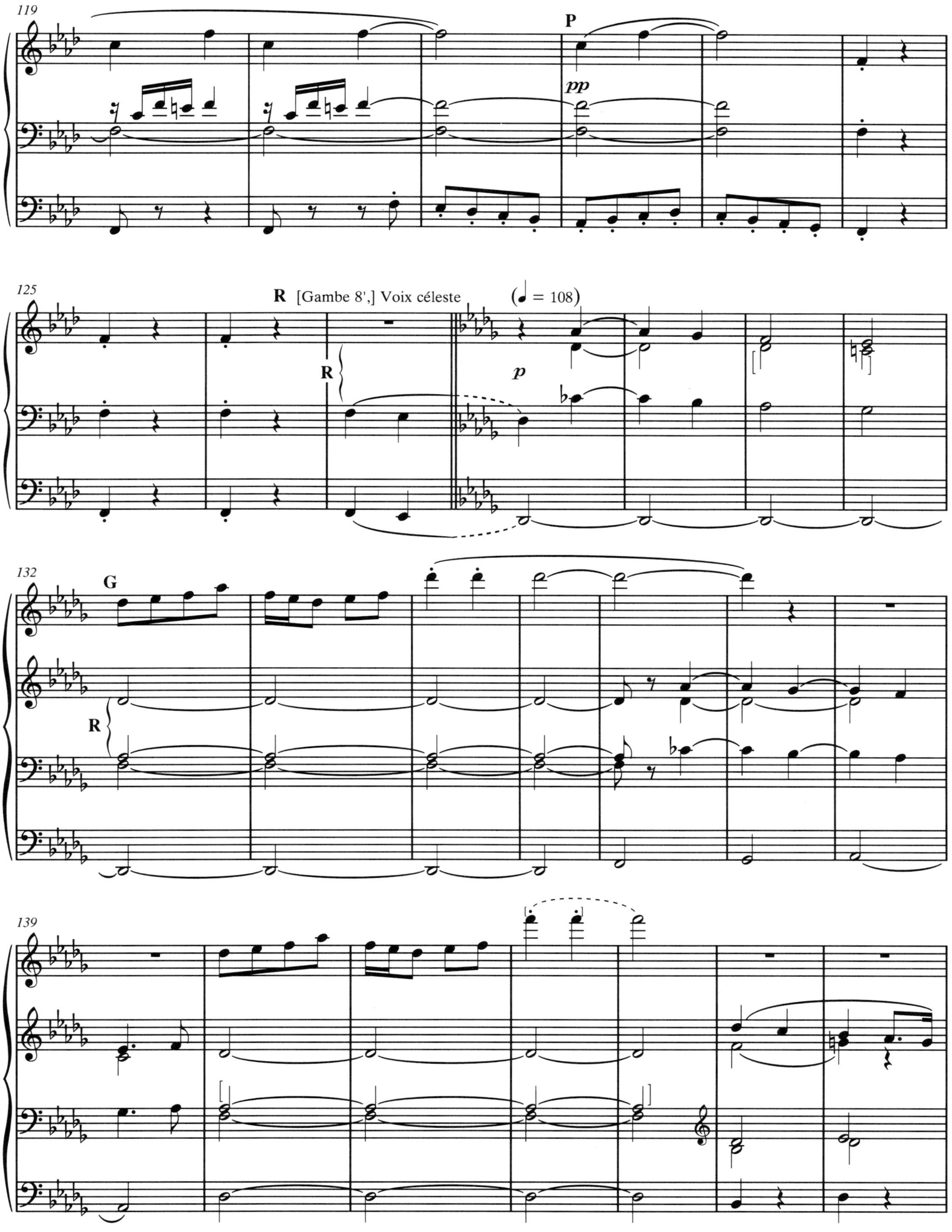
119
P
pp
125
R [Gambe 8',] Voix céleste
(♩ = 108)
R
p
132
G
R
139

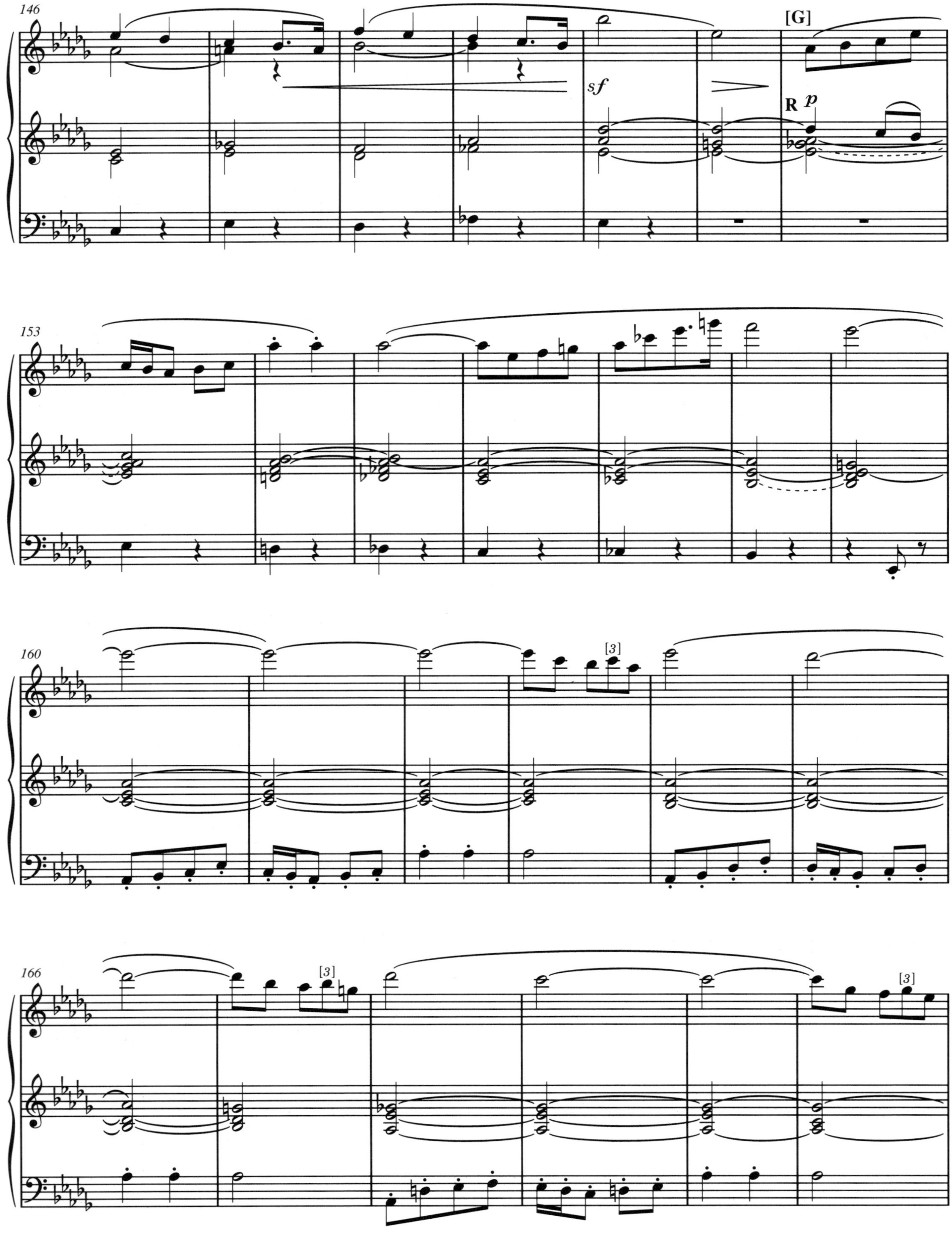
146
sf
[G]
R p
153
160
[3]
166
[3]
[3]

29

*See Critical Notes

217
meno vivo
P
f
223
(♩ = 152)
GR
228
meno vivo
P
f
(♩ =152)
R
pp
[𝄾]
234
(R Hautbois)
G solo

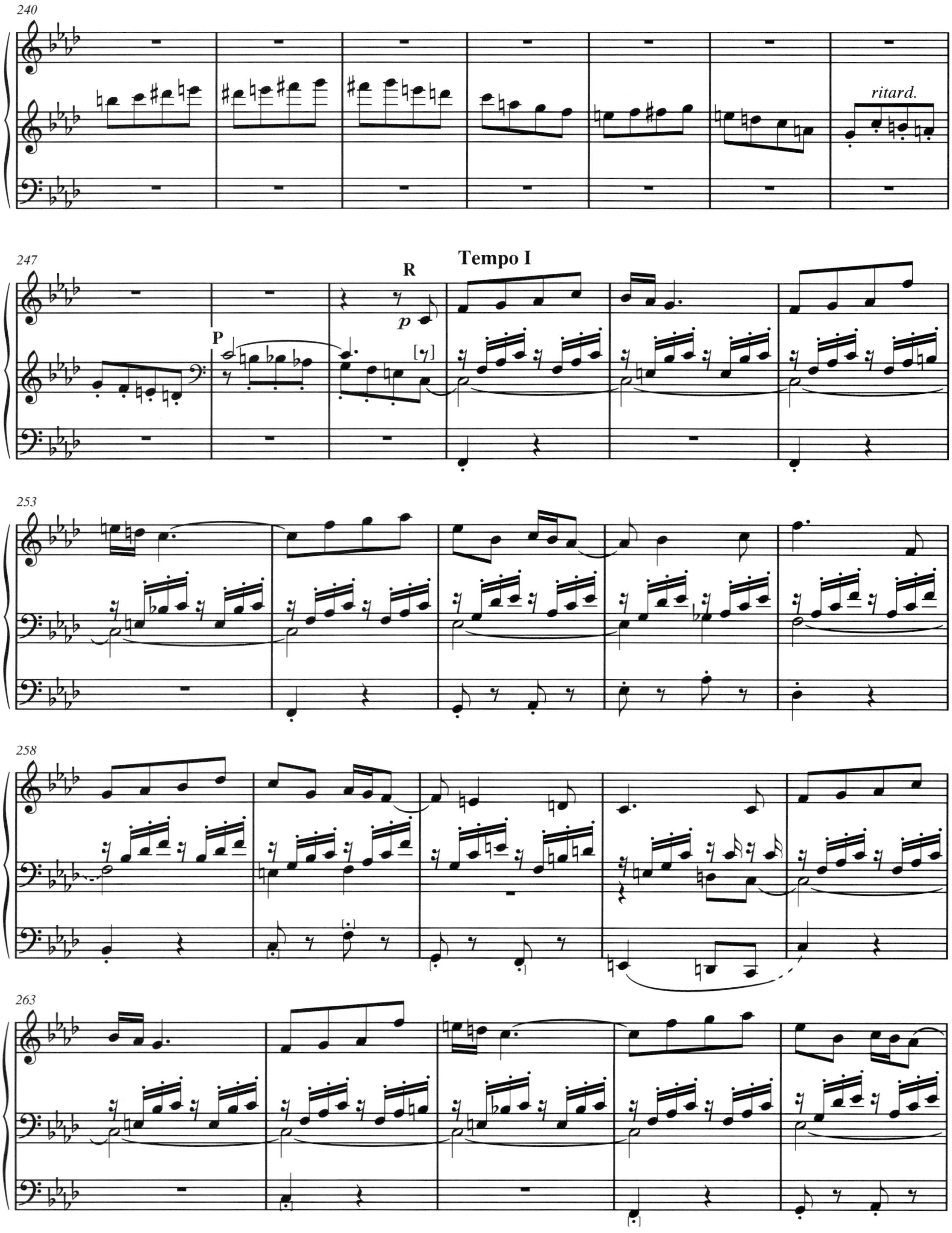
240
ritard.
247
R
Tempo I
P
p
253
258
263

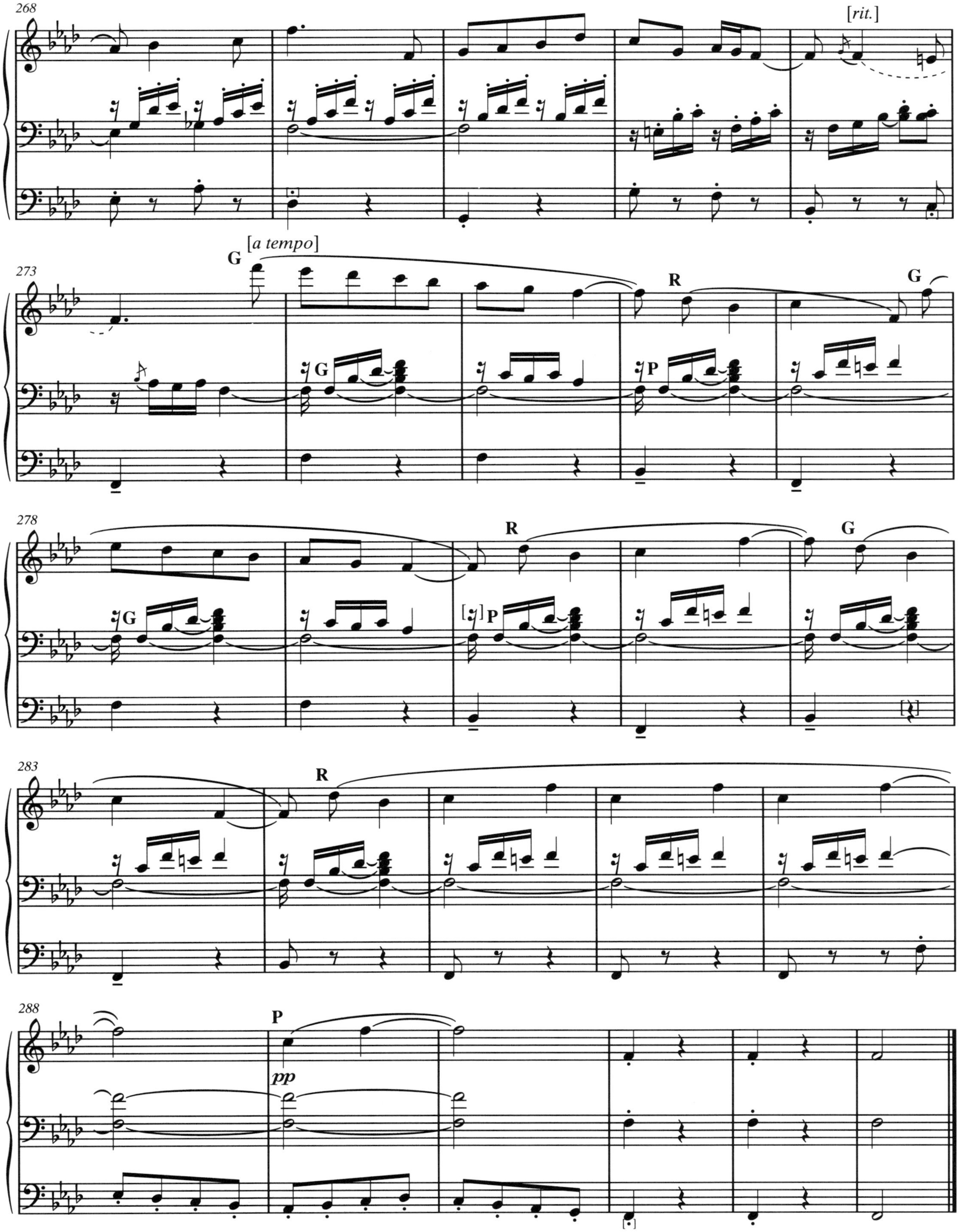
268
[rit.]
273
[a tempo]
G
R
G
P
G
278
R
G
[𝄾]
P
283
R
288
P
pp

This page has been left blank to facilitate page turns.

III

Grand orgue: Fonds 16', 8', 4'
Positif: Fonds 16', 8', 4'
Récit: Fonds 8', 4'
Pédale: Fonds 32', 16', 8', 4'

Andantino quasi allegretto (♩ = 88)

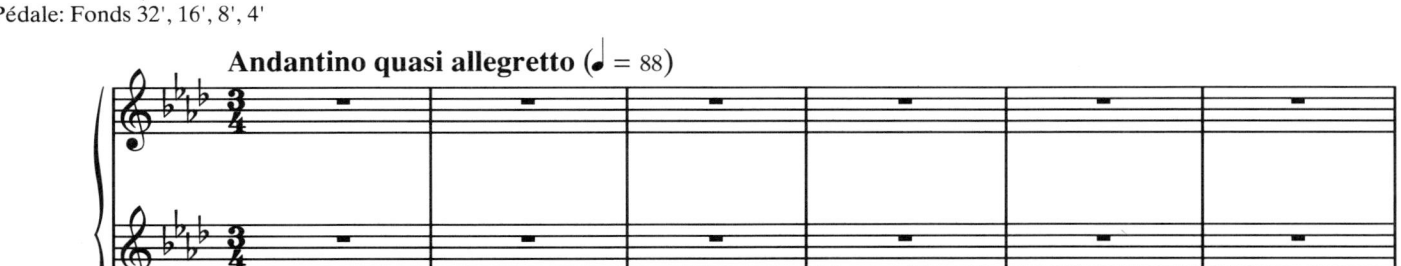

Péd. GPR *f*

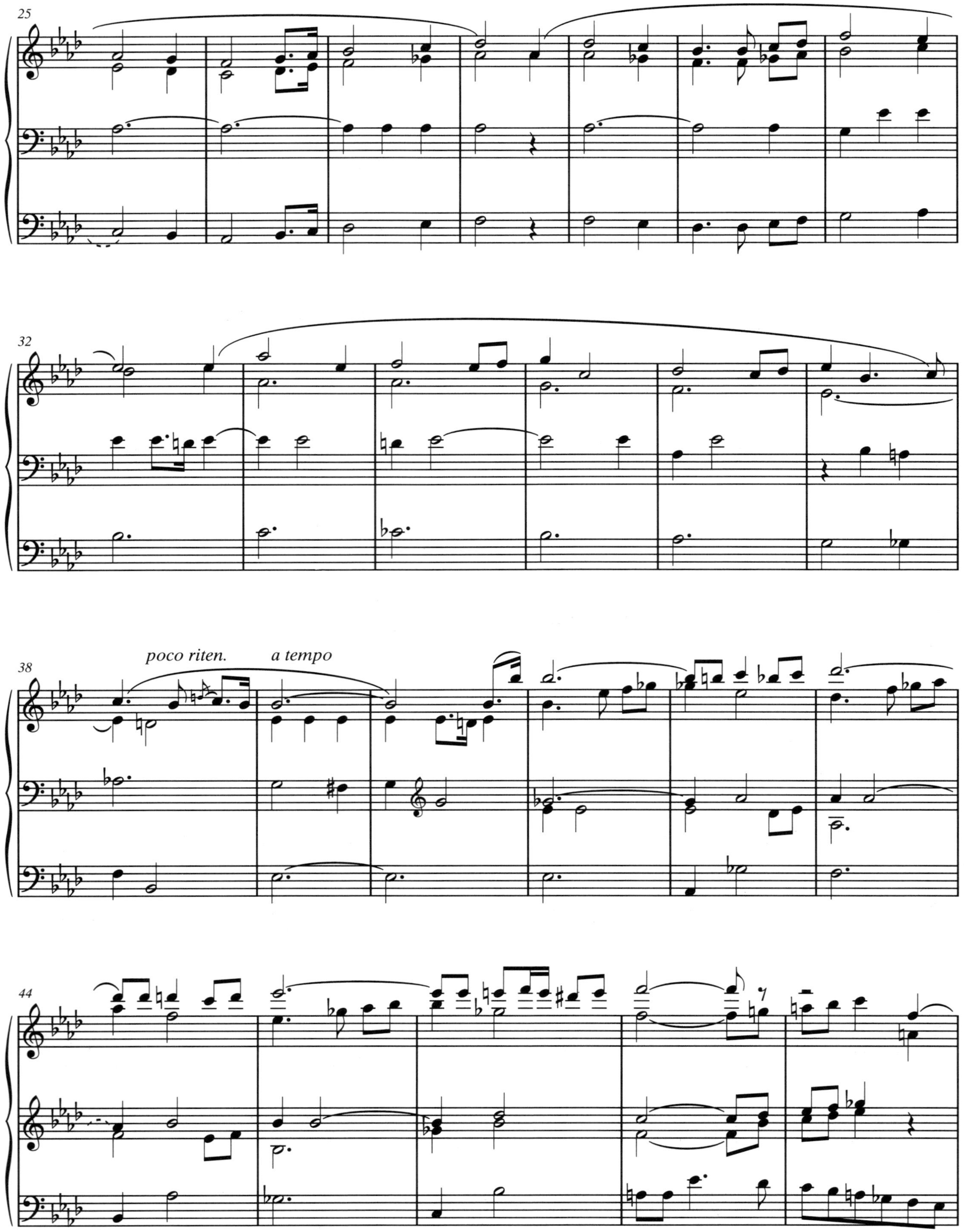
25
32
38
poco riten.
a tempo
44

49
R
55
R
p
61
(P [Fonds] 8', 4')
PR
67
Più mosso (♩ = 132)
(R Anches 16', 8', 4')
Péd. GP mf

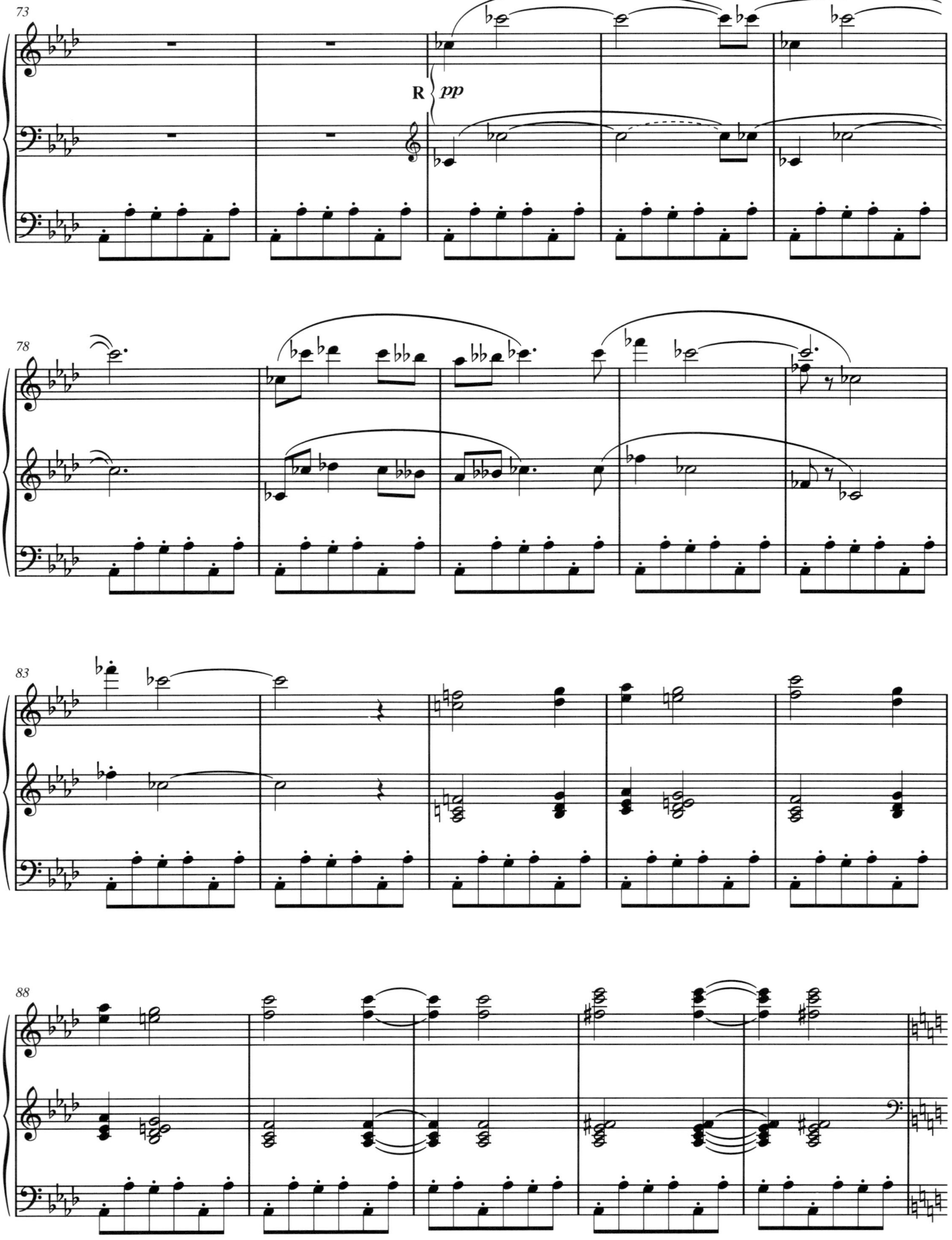
73
R
pp
78
83
88

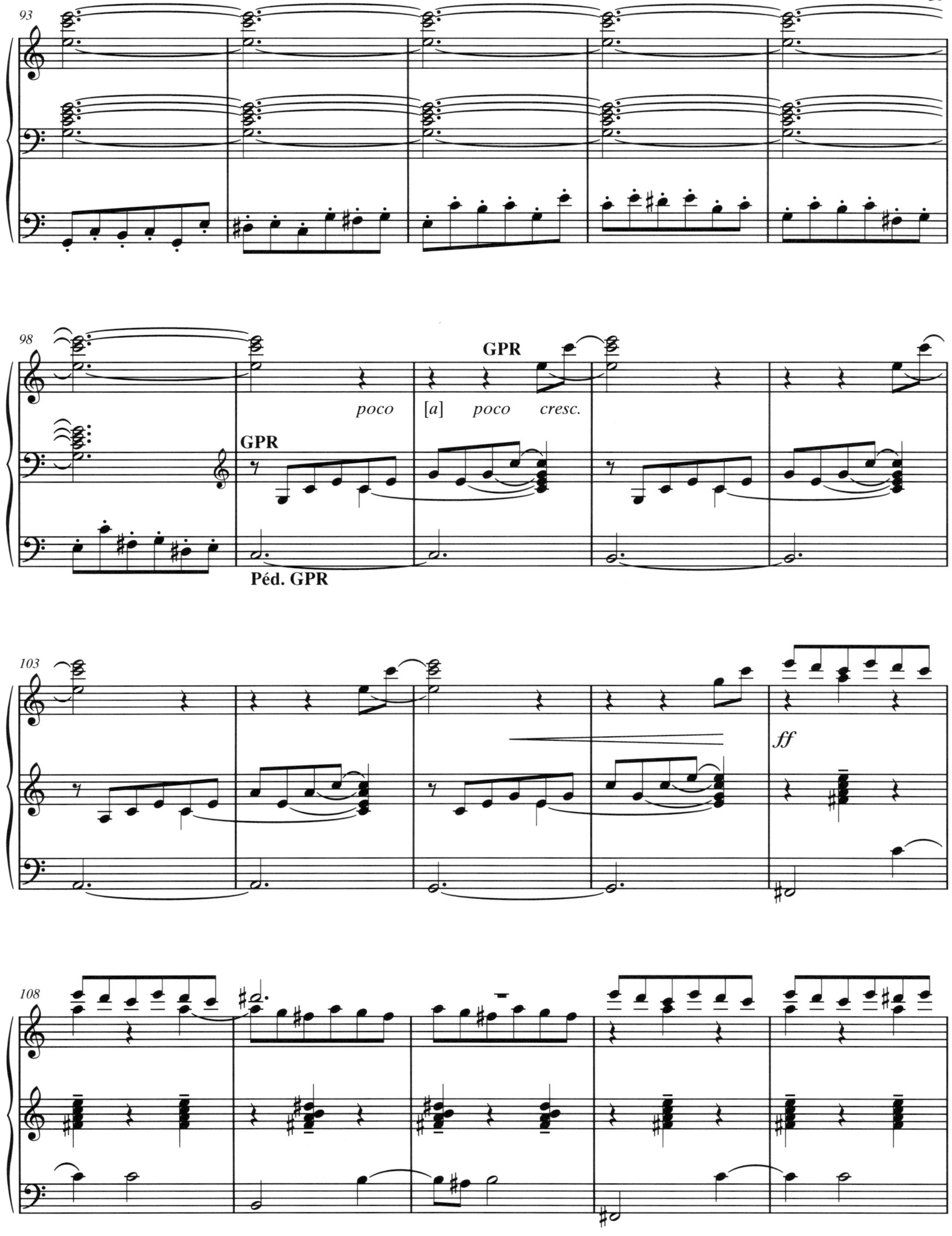
93
98
GPR
poco [a] poco cresc.
GPR
Péd. GPR
103
ff
108

40

41

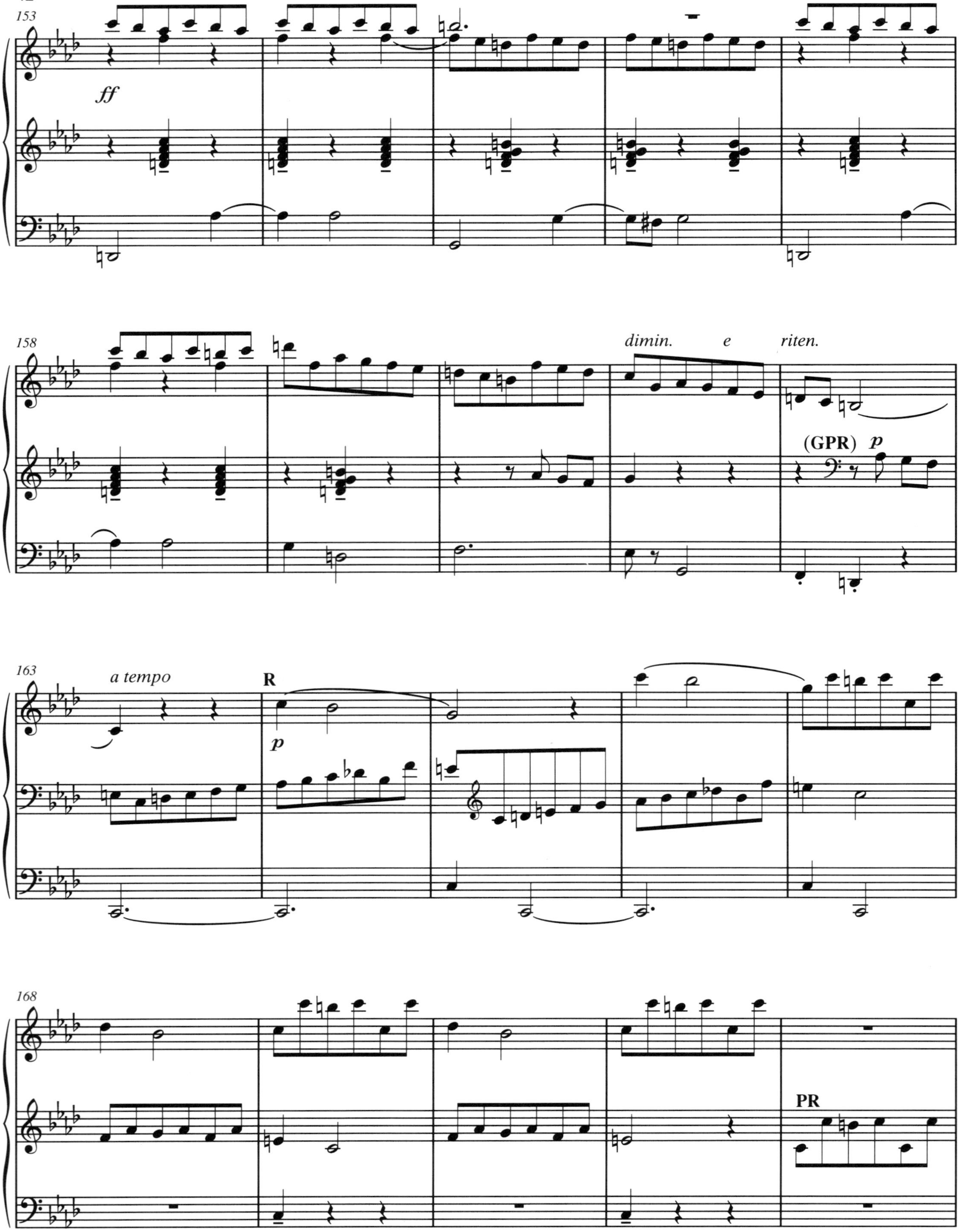
153
ff
158
dimin.
e
riten.
(GPR)
p
163
a tempo
R
p
168
PR

173
(R)
dimin. e poco ritard.
178
Tempo I
R Flûtes 8', 4'
R
pp
[3]
[6]
(Péd. Basses 16', 8')
pp
182
186
ritard. molto
tr
PR

190
a tempo
GPR
f
GPR
[Fonds] 32', 16', 8', 4'
f
196
202
poco rit.
a tempo
208

214
R
220
R
(P [Fonds] 8', 4')
p
PR
227
R
rit.
Péd. GPR
233
a tempo
P Fonds 16', 8', 4'
PR
f
239
R
[𝄐]
p

Grand orgue: Fonds 16', 8'
Récit: Gambe [8'], Voix céleste
Pédale: Flûte 4'

IV

Adagio ($\eighth = 63$)

47

V. Toccata

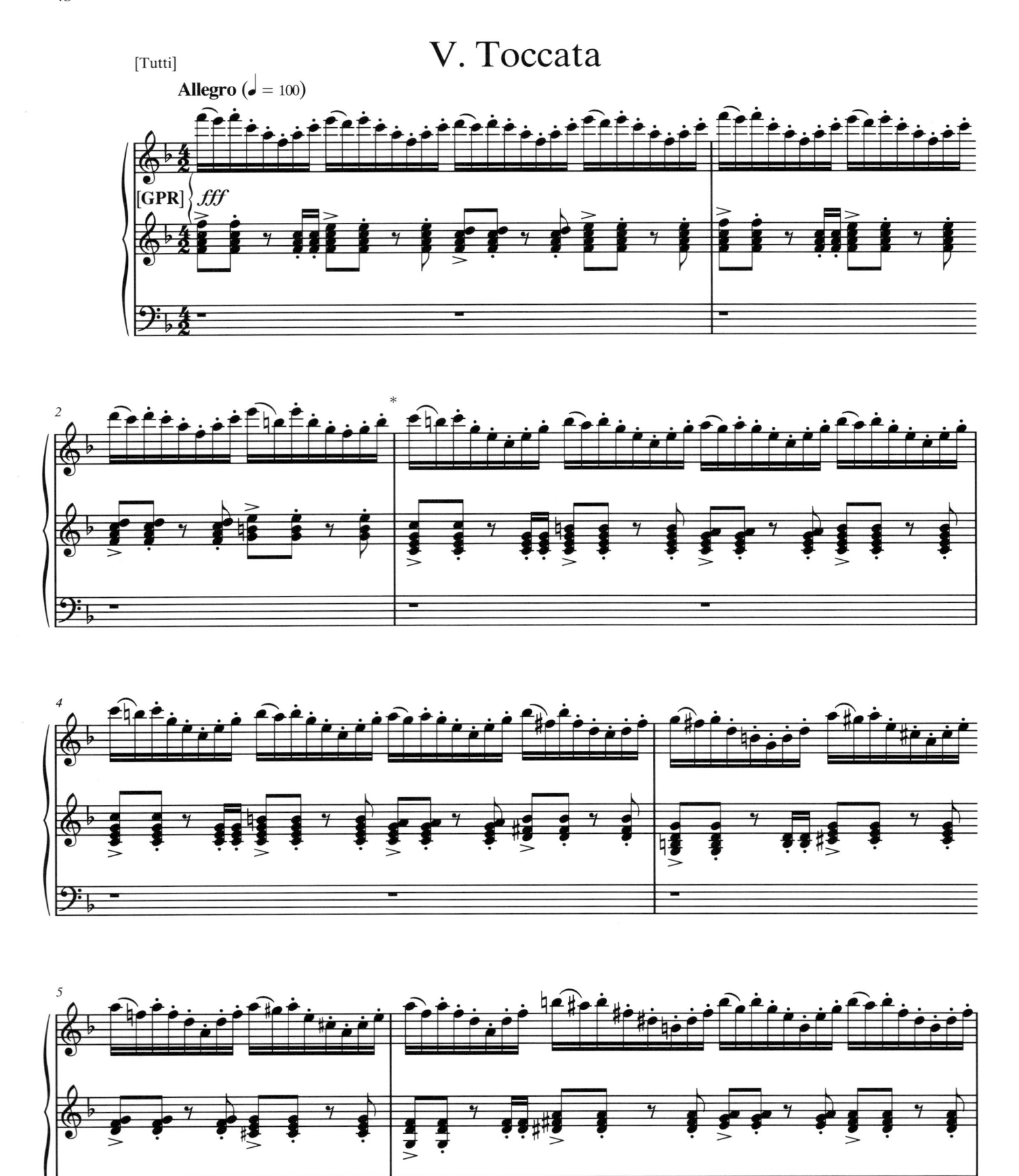

*See Critical Commentary concerning the articulation in mm. 3–75.

49

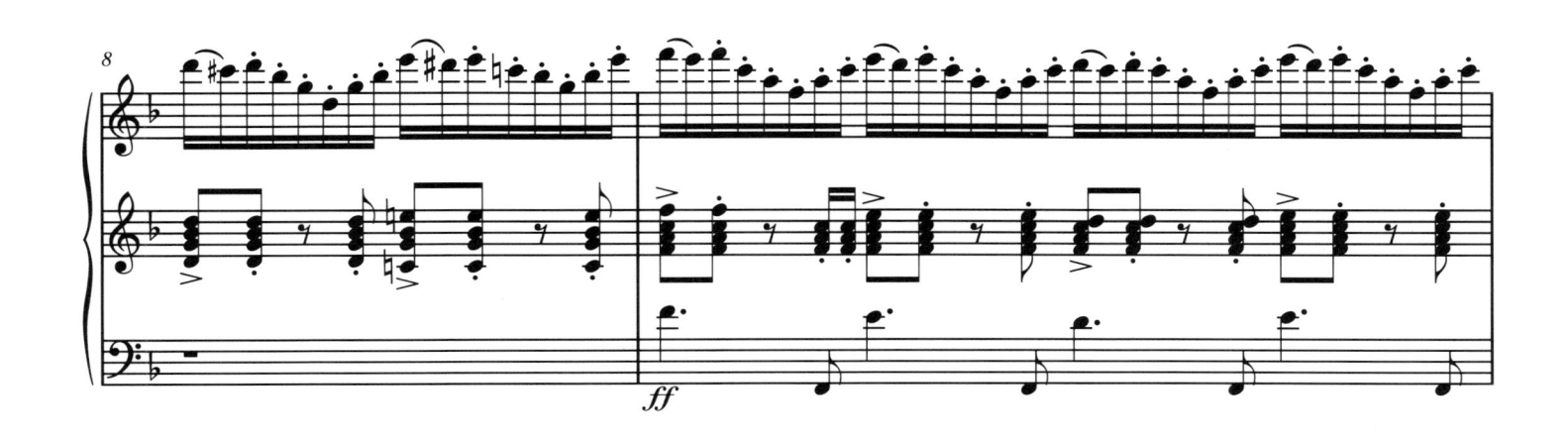

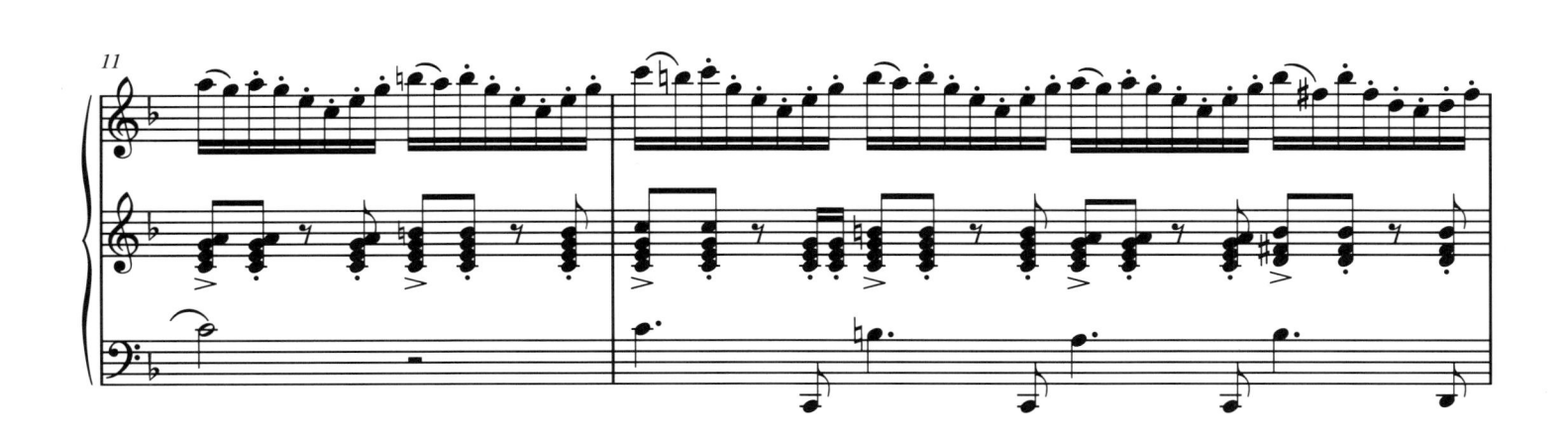

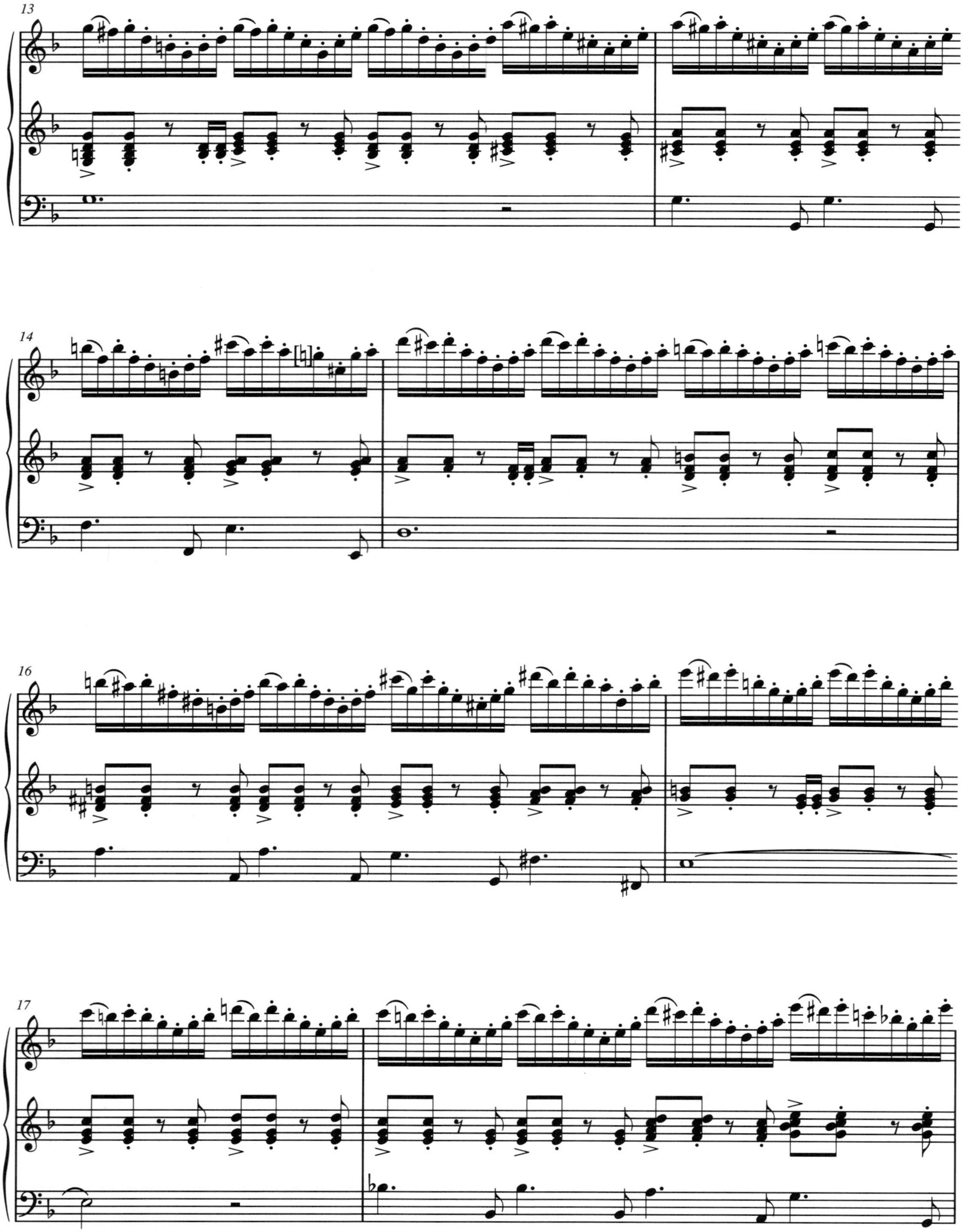

51

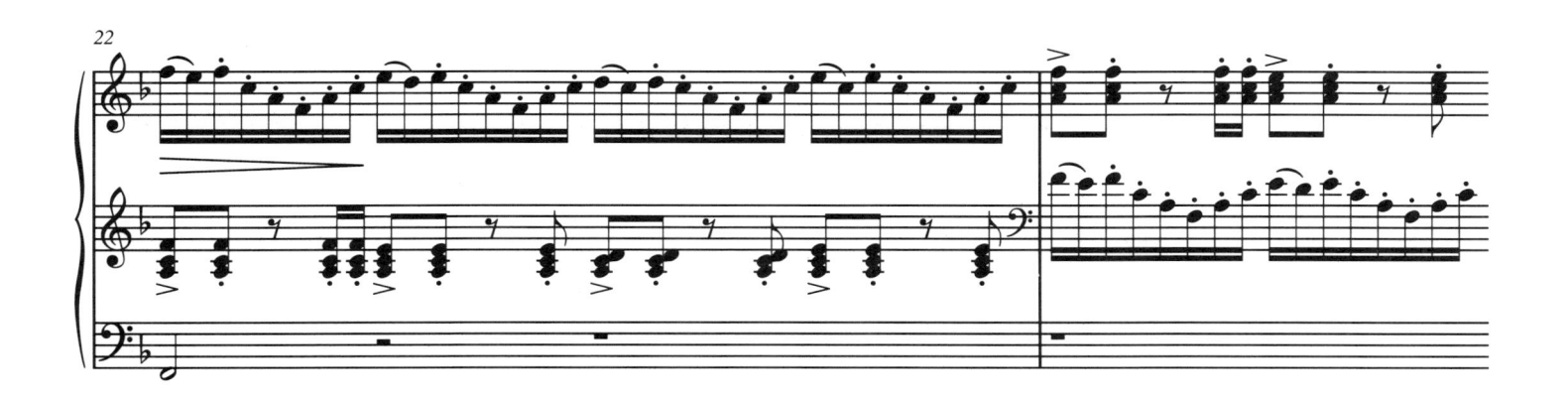

*See Critical Notes.

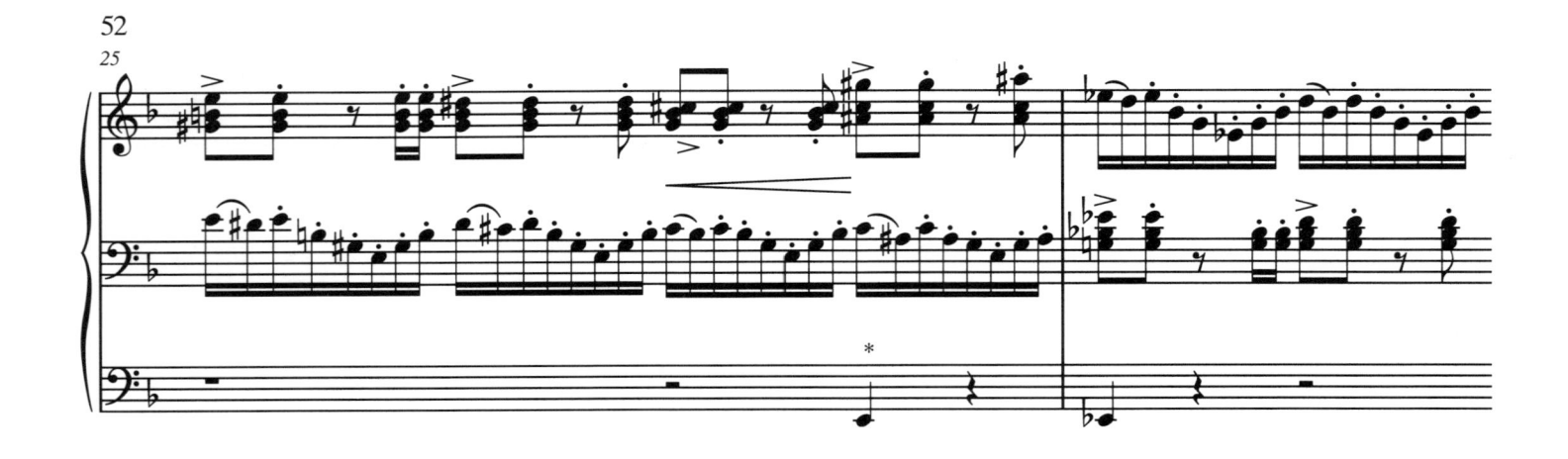

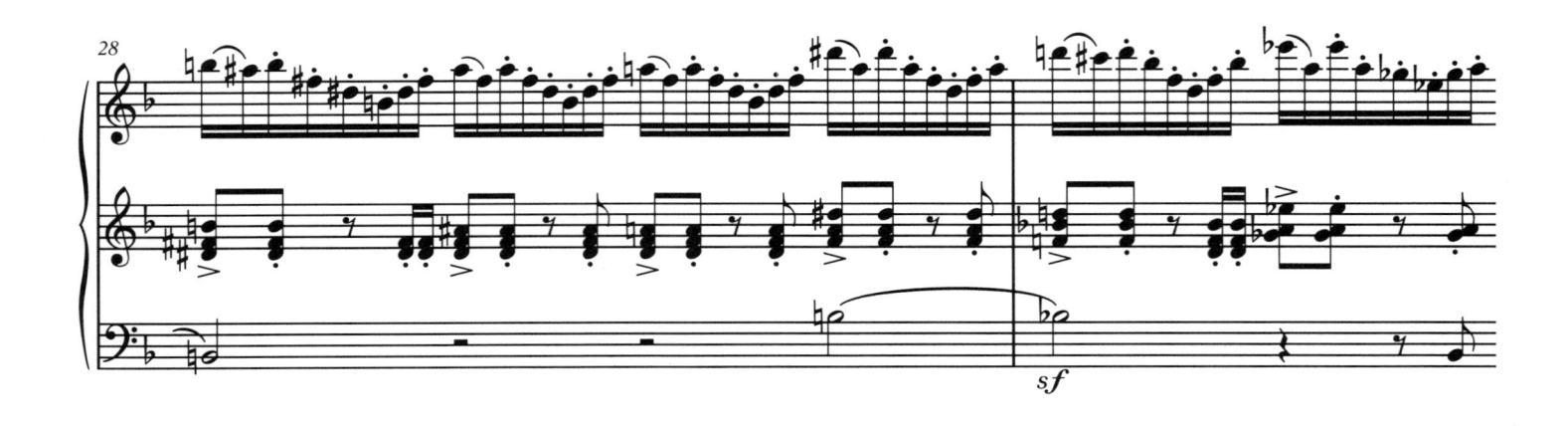

*See Critical Notes.

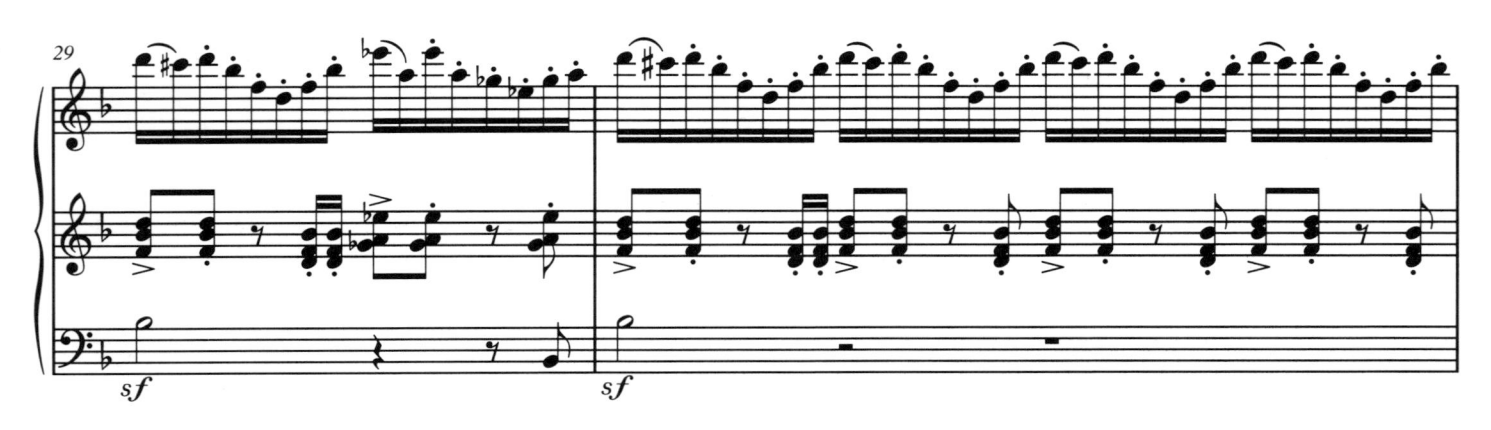

53

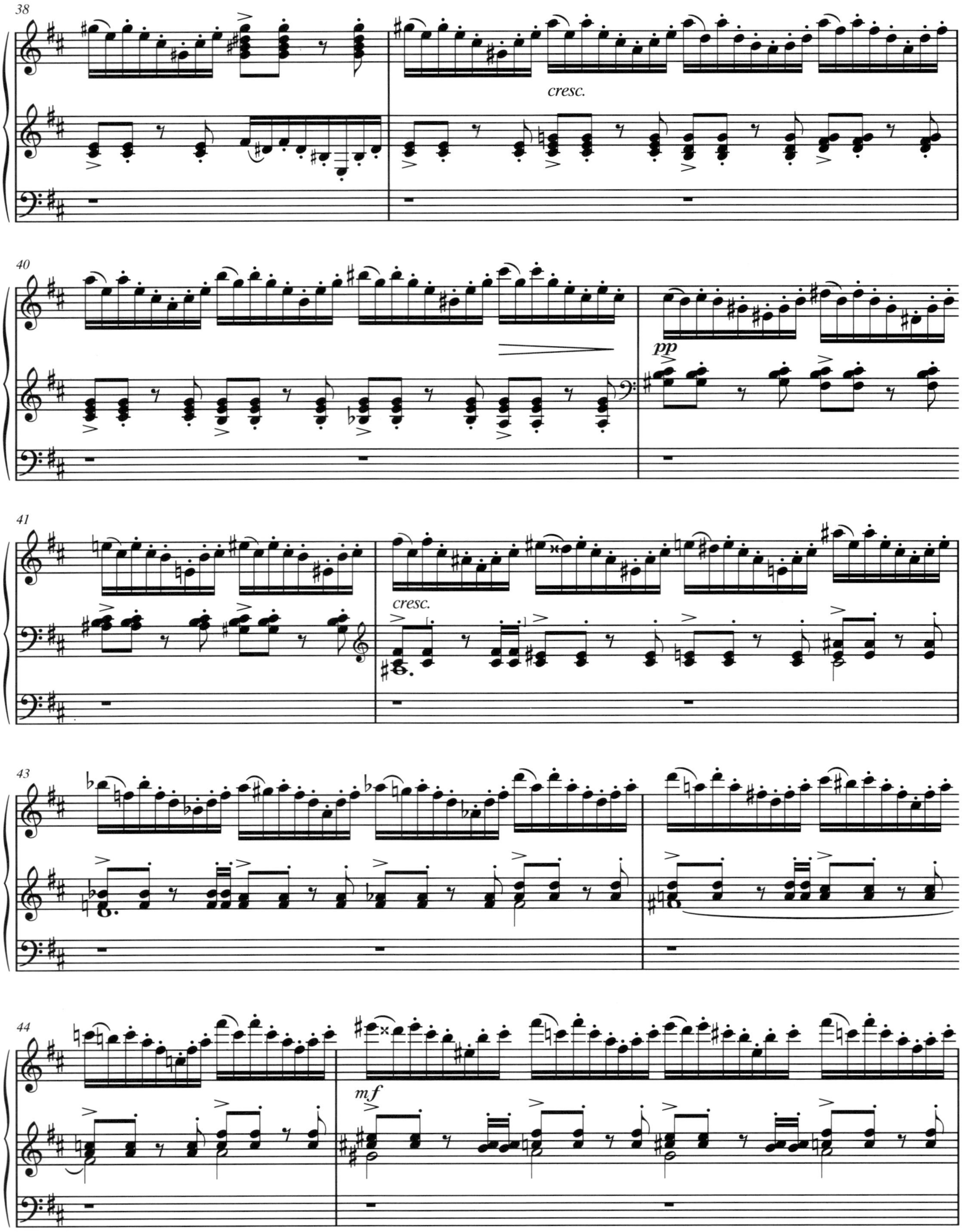
cresc.
pp
cresc.
mf

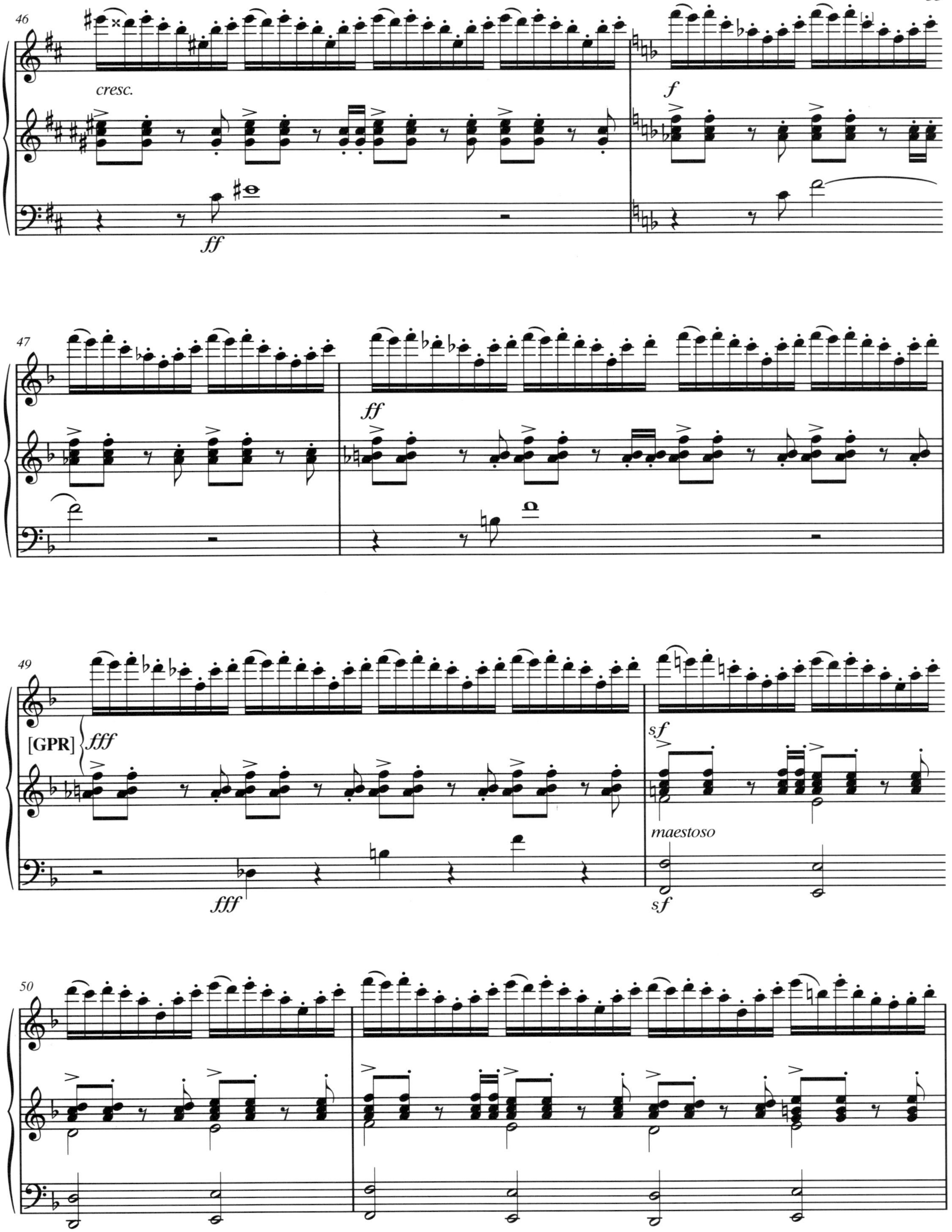
46
cresc.
ff
f
47
ff
49
[GPR]
fff
fff
sf
maestoso
sf
50

56

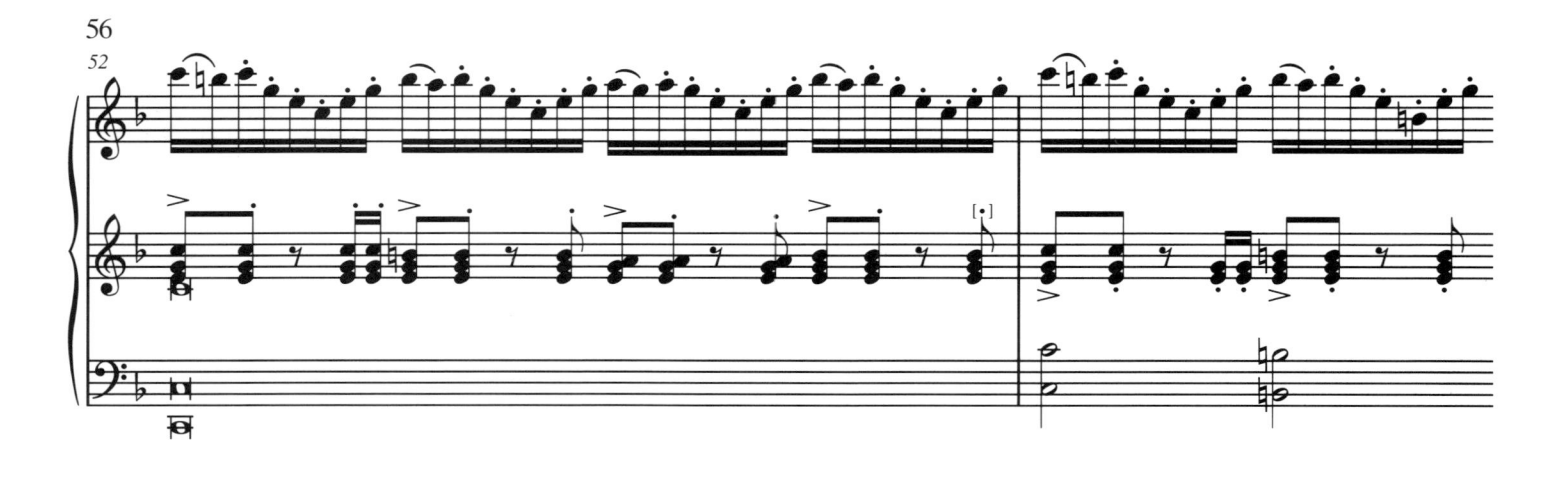

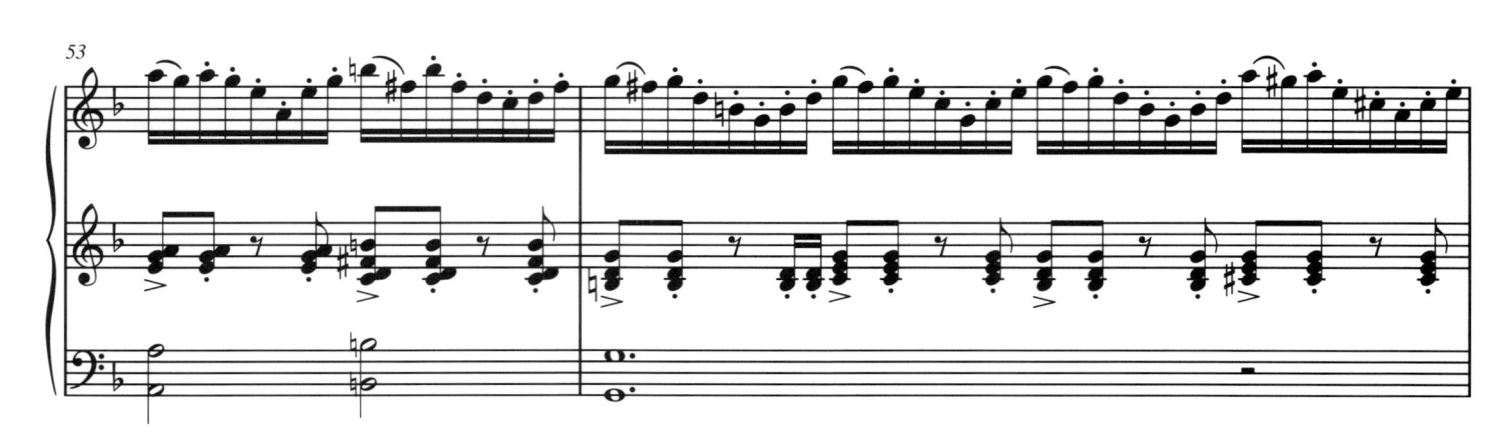

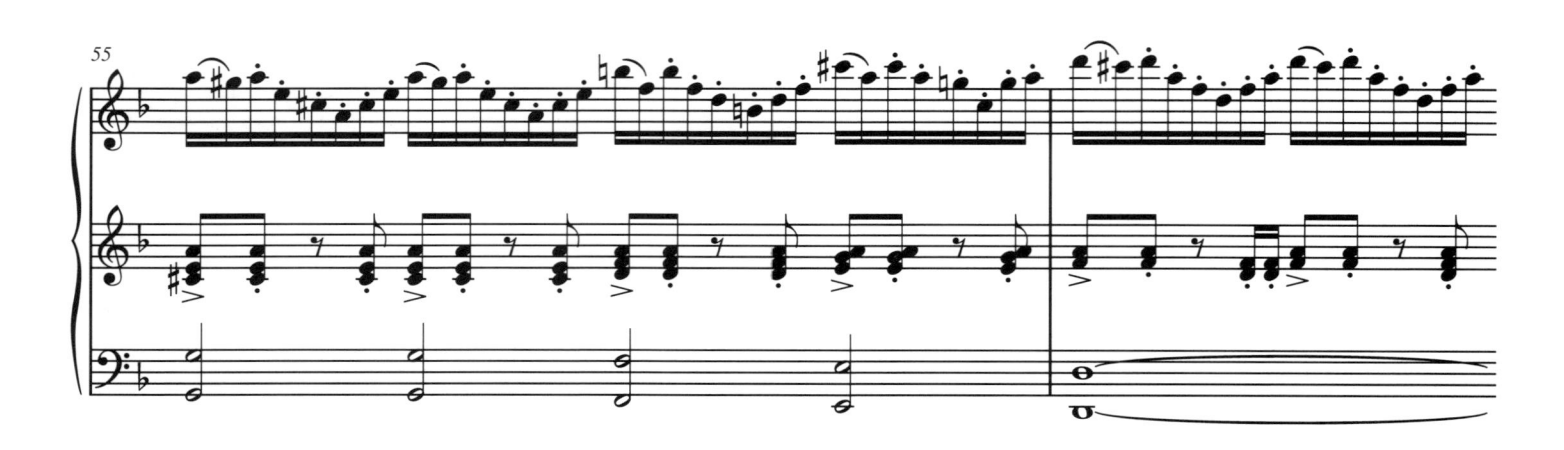

57

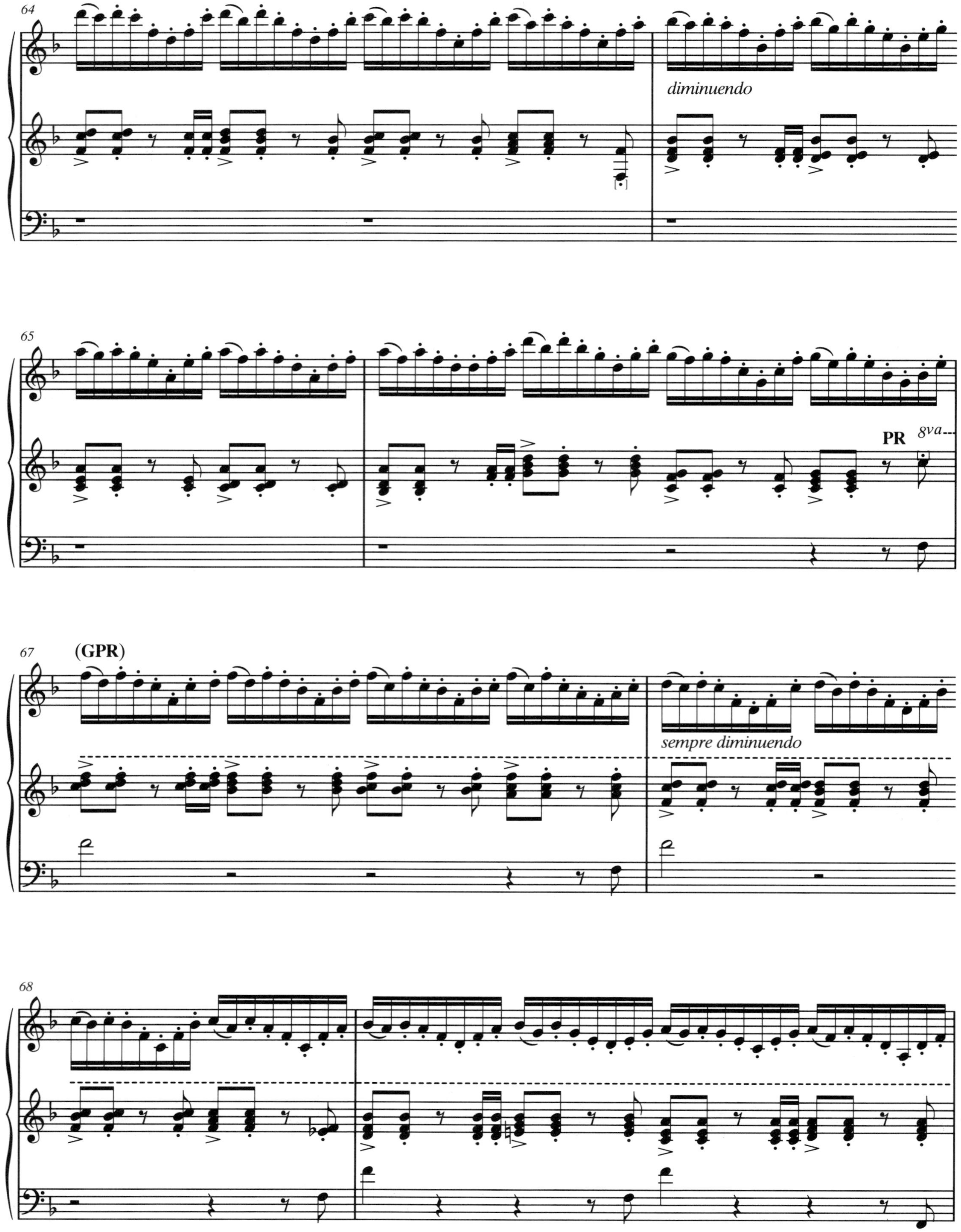
64
diminuendo
65
PR
8va
67
(GPR)
sempre diminuendo
68

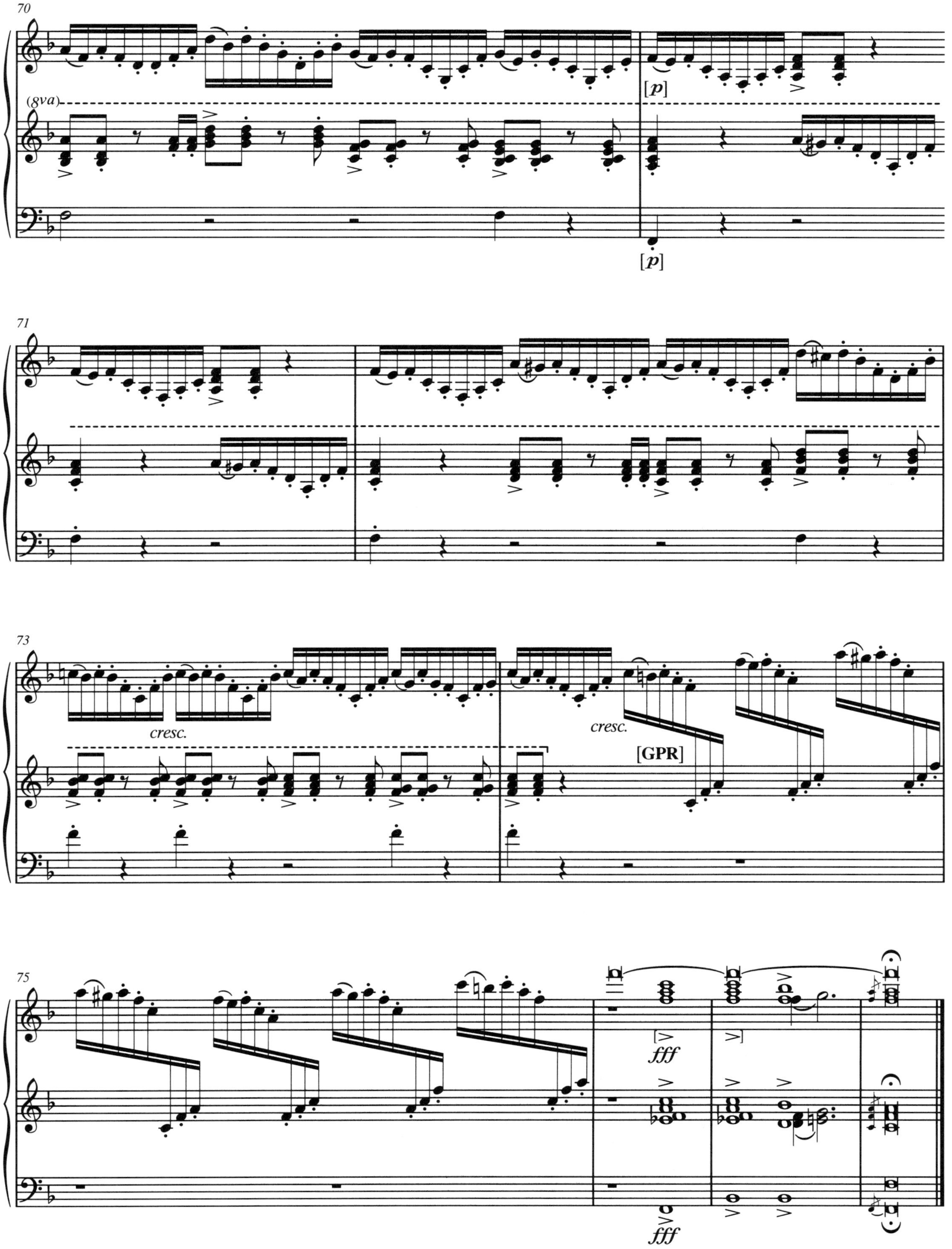
70
(8va)
[p]
[p]
71
73
cresc.
cresc.
[GPR]
75
fff
fff